Beowulf
is
my
name

Seventh-century Germanic lyre from the Sutton Hoo ship burial, East Anglia (reconstruction). See "The Sutton Hoo Lyre, *Beowulf,* and the Origins of the Frame Harp" by Rupert and Myrtle Bruce-Mitford, *Antiquity,* XLIV (March 1970). Photograph by courtesy of the Trustees of the British Museum.

Beowulf
is
my
name

*and selected translations
of other Old English poems*

A NEW VERSION
by FREDERICK R. REBSAMEN
University of Arizona

Rinehart Press
SAN FRANCISCO

SBN: 03-084555-6
Printed in the United States of America
0123   029   987654321

To the poet, whoever he was, whose song gave a richer light to that first bright flare of English civilization, this book is gratefully dedicated.

INTRODUCTION

WHAT FOLLOWS is in three parts: a Modern English version of *Beowulf,* straight prose translations of six Old English poems relevant to *Beowulf,* and a discussion of the problems involved in editing and translating Old English poetry. The second and third parts require no further comment here, but my treatment of the poem in the first part does need some explanation. This treatment grew out of the peculiarities of the poem itself, for *Beowulf* is like nothing else in literature at any time.

The nameless poet who put *Beowulf* into the form in which we know it probably lived and worked in the late seventh and early eighth centuries, was either a Christian or very familiar with and influenced by Christianity, and wrote about people and events which can be safely placed in Denmark and Sweden in the early sixth century—well before Christianity had made any real impact upon that area. The "audience" of *Beowulf*—an individual reading a manuscript or a group listening to a performance—would have been familiar with both Christian and pagan Germanic traditions, for Anglo-Saxon paganism was still very much alive in 700. Thus the poet could create a story and a central character involving the qualities of both traditions, going beyond the mere merger of pagan technique with Christian content that was first effected, according to Bede, by Caedmon in the third quarter of the seventh century.

The unique manuscript of *Beowulf* dates from around 1000 A.D., and thus was written two or three hundred years after the poem was composed. This is convenient for those who choose to find corruption in those parts of the manuscript which seem to interfere with this or that interpretation of it. It has been called a compilation of three different poems with rough seams at the points of joining; a loosely connected bundle of folktale, legend, mythology, and history; a pagan Germanic heroic epic carefully tilled by a Christian scribe who weeded out all references to pagan gods and planted Christian references in their stead;

and a poem—perhaps defective here and there, perhaps deliberately corrupted here and there, but a *poem* more or less faithful to the original composition.

This last view requires a willingness to see *Beowulf* as essentially the work of one unusually gifted poet who, as Professor Tolkien reminded everyone more than thirty years ago, built himself a highly original structure of magnificent contrast, choosing for his purpose to make his hero fight monsters instead of other heroes in the major battles. Having accepted this view, one is abruptly free to enjoy the poem as it is, and with very little effort a sympathetic reader can find much to admire. The question of whether *Beowulf* is a Christian or a pagan poem will be forever clouded by the fact that the best qualities of both these traditions overlap in such a way that no clash is felt, and it must ultimately be decided by reference to the whole, its aggregate effect upon the emotions. But this question, as well as others, should first be directed at that feature of the poem which is the most fascinating thing about it: Beowulf himself.

It seems clear to me that the poet has here created for his purpose a character who would not have been recognized in the poet's day as any particular figure from history or legend or folklore or mythology— though this assumption must ultimately be accepted on faith. Beowulf is neither human nor superhuman, Christian nor pagan, English nor Geatish, heroic nor humble, but something of all of these and much more besides. To the standard Germanic heroic attributes, all of which Beowulf has, the poet has added a measure of compassion and understanding and meditative restraint which, although these same qualities were certainly to be found to one degree or another in some real-life Germanic heroes, has made of Beowulf as a *literary* character something approaching Chaucer's knight. *Approaching*, I say, for the differences are of course enormous and the cultures eight hundred years apart—yet Beowulf, to a reflective reader familiar with both cultures, really does come across as, in his own day and way, "a verray parfit gentil knyght." The big difference here is that we *expect* Chaucer's knight to be all these things; with Beowulf, it is the unexpected.

The puzzling things about Beowulf's life—his origin, the fact that he apparently never married and/or produced any children, his return alone from the battle that took the life of his lord, his apparent inactivity during the later Geat-Swede conflicts—these, together with the ambiguous qualities mentioned above, cease to be bothersome when one accepts the idea that, after all, his creator was a major poet trying something big and new, involving the best standards of two different ways of life, and that his concentration upon theme and mood has made of Beowulf, in places, a puzzling character. If the reader further accepts, as I do, the idea that the poet was here presenting his personal elegy for the demise of an old and in many ways admirable tradition at the moment when it was giving into and merging its best qualities with a new one, then Beowulf as a character grows less and less puzzling and begins to make very good sense indeed.

For these reasons I have in my treatment of the poem taken some liberties with the central character. First of all, I have presented the whole in the first person, from Beowulf's point of view, simply because it seemed to me that it worked better that way. Secondly, I have gone beyond the poem, especially in the final third of it, by putting words into Beowulf's mouth by way of expressing his reactions to events. Indeed, I have taken the scant references to Hygelac's last battle —those in the poem and those in three medieval Latin manuscripts—and constructed an entire scene including the voyage from Götland to the Rhine (with a storm along the way), the battle itself, and Beowulf's escape, precisely because Beowulf has become for me such a vivid character that I presumed to guess at what he was thinking about at that moment.

As for the rest, I have done a number of things to make this presentation of the poem as clear and self-sufficient as I could without destroying its general effect. In order to help the unspecialized reader to a better understanding of what the poem is all about, I have freely incorporated into my translation much information gathered through books and a year's study and travel in Europe: descriptions of ships and armor, geographical precisions, historical references, details of topography and architecture, and numerous small embellishments throughout. I have even, in the best tradition of the medieval poet, stolen lines from other Old English poems when they seemed to add enrichment. I have kept all of the "digressions" because they were essential to the poem, but I have clarified most of them and rearranged the sequence of many. In retelling this story from Beowulf's point of view, I have consistently referred to the poet who created *Beowulf* as "the poet," and to poets who figure *within Beowulf* as "the minstrel" or "Hrothgar's minstrel." And finally, I have *not* changed any of the numerous references to the Christian God by Danes and Geats who are clearly described as heathen by both history and the *Beowulf* poet himself. This is not as confusing as it probably seems to the modern reader and, along with the relative positions of God and Fate in the poem, should not be allowed to detract from the total effect.

I mostly hope that the sympathetic reader may absorb the poem as here presented with something like the pleasure and intrigue and uplifting of the heart that it must have offered to an Anglo-Saxon audience, though the pace of the poetry and the sound of the harp must here be sacrificed. *Beowulf* stands at the beginning of English civilization and English poetry— "between the worlds," as R. W. Chambers said. It salutes the dying of the old and the birth of the new, and belongs to every man whose native tongue is English.

For all that I have done to the poem here, I offer no apology. It has been a labor of love and respect, conceived in honor of the nameless poet and delivered as a tribute to his memory.

Although I had the pleasure of reading *Beowulf* in the original manuscript through the courtesy of the British Museum, my translation has been based primarily upon four great editions of the poem: those of E. V. K. Dobbie, F. Klaeber, C. L. Wrenn, and A. J. Wyatt as revised by R. W. Chambers. For personal courtesy and expense of valuable time I offer much thanks to Hans Ole Hansen, director of the Historisk-Arkaeologisk Forsøgscenter in Lejre, Denmark; Ole Crumlin-Petersen, director of the Vikingeskibshallen in Roskilde, Denmark; Ulf Erik Hagberg of the Statens Historiska Museum in Stockholm, Sweden; and Mrs. Anne Sofie Gräslund of Uppsala University in Sweden. To Miss Myrtle Bruce-Mitford, for her generous and patient response to my questions about the Sutton Hoo lyre, which was at that time still under reconstruction in her laboratory in the British Museum, I am especially grateful.

Finally, I must acknowledge the staggering obligation I have assumed in writing this book. From every book-length study of *Beowulf* ever published, from numerous translations of the poem, from a hundred other books upon subjects related to *Beowulf*, from at least two hundred articles and monographs, and of course from all of the modern editions of the poem, I have freely and gratefully borrowed the thoughts and conclusions of others. I should repeat that I have not merely translated the poem; I have also deliberately altered the sequence of events, clarified digressions, inserted much background information, put thoughts and reactions into Beowulf's head, and chosen to read many passages in ways suggested by authors and editors that, in the absence of conclusive evidence, seemed somehow right to me. These authors and editors, as well as students of *Beowulf*, will recognize all of the things that I have taken from others. Specific credits would have cluttered nearly every page, and a necessarily enormous bibliography would have been no help to anyone. I can only say that, for all of this help from so many people, I am immensely grateful.

Frederick Rebsamen

Tucson, Arizona
March 1970

contents

illustrations

The sketches and photographs on the following pages are by O. Sörling, W. Meijer, and E. Hansen, and the Justus Cederquists Company and are reproduced from Bernhard Salin's *Die Altgermanische Thierornamentik*, translated from the original Swedish by J. Mestorf, published by Wahlström and Widstrand, Stockholm, 1935. Reprinted by permission.

I

Beowulf Is My Name

PROLOGUE

Twelve men rode round his barrow all in a ring,
Singing of him what they could understand.
—RICHARD WILBUR

I AM HYGELAC'S hearth-companion;
Beowulf is my name. Sometimes I merely rest and
avoid thought, feel as if I do, yet do not, exist.
Sometimes I find myself marching through the fields
of Zealand, yet speaking an alien tongue. My gods
are the gods of Northern men, and I can see them in

the green shoots of spring, hear them in the snarl and slash of storms, and feel them in my arm as I lift my spear and draw it back for hurling—yet at times I speak of only one. Sometimes I myself feel something like a god—and sometimes I am like the morning fog as it slowly vanishes before the rising sun. At such moments I reach for my sword but grasp nothing; call my father's name but get no answer; search for my bountiful king but cannot think where he is.

The finest moments come when I am awakened from a long sleep by the sweet plucking of harp strings and the strong clear voice of the poet, calling my name: "Beowulf, son of Ecgtheow. He was a good king!" And then I remember Hygelac, my lord, and how on winter nights I would walk the length of the hall and stop before his throne, bend to kiss him, kneel and place my hand and head upon his knee. The fire cracks and hisses upon the hearth, rousing the hawks asleep in the high beams, and now and then one stretches his strong wings and makes a turn through the long room. Outside the snow drifts steadily down and the grey wolf, trembling with cold and hunger, crouches and howls at the edge of light, and the raven screams in circles above him. Inside the hall where I sit beside my lord it is warm with the fire and the bright sounds of laughter; together we take the cups of ale from the white, ringed hands of Hygd.

But then the harp strikes a darker chord and the poet says again, "He was a good king!" And I remember how my lord was struck with swords and his son Heardred after him. I have no son; I cannot remember begetting a son; I can remember no queen, but only the long thin years, the fifty years of my reign, and then I stand again with shield and sword before the flaming serpent.

No son to take the sound of my name and carry it down: Beorhtwulf, Beaduwulf, Bealdor, I could have made so many fine names for my sons.

But there are still those moments when I can feel the strength and courage and wisdom move together in my head, and rich evening laughter of good men rises from the benches towards the dozing hawks in the beams above as the poet touches his harp and calls for me. Then I know that Beowulf is my name, and I in my youth with the strength of thirty men in my hand am proud and ready, and will sail again.

ONE

FROM SAILORS I learned of Hrothgar's grief. The great king of the Danes had once been kind to my father, so that between the Geats and Danes, across the waves from Götland to Zealand, gifts rode the summer sea. It seemed a hard fate for the king of such a great nation.

"Yes!" says the poet, "we have heard about those Danes with their spears in their hands, and what a glory they worked with them!"

Glory it was, with the great hall of Hrothgar at the bright top of it all. The poet remembers the old stories, tells how Hrothgar came to be king, this way —

A very long time ago the Danes were ruled by a good man, strong and wise as a king should be, fair and affectionate with his thanes, holding his realm together in peace with a generous hand. His son was a prince of the father's kind, and the hearts of the Danes were at rest. When the king died they wept for the sound of his voice, heaped treasures upon his breast, and sent him away with love and gold — then stopped their tears and turned to the fine young prince, quick and strong, wise for one so young. Heremod was his name, and at first he showed the good head he had received from his father — but that head soon turned, and blood ran darker than wine in the courtyard. Heremod had no gifts for his thanes except the slash of sharp-filed swords and the bite of spears; he robbed and murdered his own men in his own hall and died with a curse on his lips. "He was misled by wicked giants," as the poet says, and went to join their kind in Hell.

It was a long bad time for the Danes. They bowed their heads in lordless misery, for Heremod had left no heir — and there is no grief among men of the North as cold and sharp as the grief of an empty throne. Then the Ruler saw their sorrow and made a change in Fate, sent to the Danes a child in a boat with a sheaf of new grain beside his head.

Scyld was the name they gave him as he grew up, for they could see in him the signs of a great king and knew that he would be a shield to them all. Scyld Scefing he came to be called, who arrived with a sheaf of grain and a new year.

He grew to the throne as surely as ivy reaches to the high gable. To hostile tribes he offered war, and won. To friends he offered help and protection. From all he demanded allegiance and respect, and soon was receiving tribute from far across the lakes and channels. Rich and famous, loved and feared, he became what the poets call "a good king," in which phrase all royal virtues are gathered.

A son was born to that throne and given the name of Beowulf, though I carry no blood of his in my veins and was not named for him. He grew up as a prince of full promise, learned how to hold and share his wealth, and made the hearts of his men his own. And then it was time for Scyld to return to the place he had come from — though no one knew where that might be.

They laid him in a boat, as he had asked. They placed him close by the mast and heaped upon his heart gold-hilted swords and plated helmets, golden rings and bracelets, jeweled cups and drinking horns, gleaming gray corslets and spears, silver spoons and dishes from the East and patterned brooches from the South, clasps and buckles set with garnets for his robes, and gold coins from many countries. Then they placed a silver bowl near his hand, and high above his head upon the mast a golden banner. They shoved the boat into the sea and watched it float away towards the place from which that other boat had come long before. No one could say who would receive that precious gift.

The years grew glorious for the Danes; into their courts came the best men of the North. Beowulf had a son and named him Healfdene because his mother was of another nation, and this son grew up to be greater than any before him. The Danes were in high fortune, each king surpassing the one before. This Healfdene had three sons—Heorogar and Hrothgar and Halga—and a daughter who was given in marriage to Prince Onela of the Swedes. Healfdene died and Heorogar took the throne as eldest son, but he died early and left the kingdom to Hrothgar. Hrothgar and the young nobles grew up together, learned the ways of swords and spears and yelled at the waves as they raced their horses along the shores of Zealand—so that when Hrothgar came into the wisdom necessary to a throne and spread his power far across the mountains and the waters, he had always around him that company of excellent earls as friends and servants with equal devotion to both offices.

Then it came to him one day that he should build the greatest hall that sons of men had ever seen, and from its high-seat give out rings and bracelets to young and old alike according to their merit, as a king should do. The orders went out, and those with skill in their hands came to offer it to the king.

Stones were cut and laid in a double wall to make the strong foundation, great logs of birch and pine were locked together with thick forged bands of iron, and oaken beams joined the walls; inside, two rows of holes were dug to receive the pillar posts, and the rafters were shoved tightly down against the mighty walls. The gables were crossed at the ends like huge horns, and over it all lay the long field of closely woven thatch and turf against rain and snow. Craftsmen paved the floor with flat stones, built benches along the two sides; they raised the king's throne, the high-seat, in the center of one side to face the large open fireplace ringed with stones in the center of the floor. And finally came the goldsmiths to plate the benches and the horned gables high above to catch the sunlight and signal far and wide the wealth and power of those who sat inside.

Then it was ready. Hrothgar shaped a name for it and called it Heorot, the "Hall of the Hart." Within, from his high throne, he welcomed Danes and Swedes and Geats, Franks and Frisians and Jutes, men of all nations of the North, and at times a man from the South or East speaking a strange tongue and bringing glass and hunks of spotted steel for the smith's hammer. Gold came steadily in to fill the hoard with twisted bars and linked rings, and from all around came the cups and bracelets and necklaces; to all who came in friendship and to his men as reward for their loyal service, he gave from this treasure. The benches were crowded with the best men of that country and there was no bad heart among them. It was not yet time, as the poet says, for the hatred of swords to strike between Hrothgar and his son-in-law, for the flames to eat that mighty building.

And then it began to happen. A misbegotten and alien creature dwelling in darkness at the edge of life could not bear the sound of the harp and the song of Hrothgar's minstrel, the laughter and the applause of happy men. To where he prowled in shadows along the edges of the moor came the sweet clear voice of the minstrel, singing of the earth's creation:

"The Almighty wrought the earth, the beautiful

bright meadows, embraced it with water, set high in glory the sun and moon as lamps of light for men, decked the regions of the earth with limbs and leaves, and shaped a life for every living thing that moves."

Outside the light and warmth of the hall, beyond the gentle grassy meadows, on the edge of darkness, Grendel roamed. Around that gilded center of life and song he circled, his angry exile from the world of men boiling black in his blood.

"In the home of monsters he lived, unhappy creature," says the poet, "since the Creator had banished him among the kin of Cain in vengeance for the death of Abel. Cain could take no pleasure from that murder, for the Maker banished him in far exile from mankind. From his sprang all kinds of miscreated elves and giants and walking spirits to struggle long against God in their hateful misery with slaughter in their dark hearts, for which He gave them a fitting reward."

He could not bear such light and laughter for very long; and so one night as shadows shoved across the meadows to wrap the hall in darkness, Grendel crept into the open and moved most like a mist towards the gentle light of the low fire. The great door jumped open at his touch and he found a troop of noble Danes sleeping on the benches after their feast and beer—there was no grieving rage on their sleeping faces, no misery of loneliness and exile in their peaceful breathing. He could not bear it. Nearly smoking with the force of his rage he snatched up fifteen men from their rest and crunched and swallowed them all before they were fully awake, then grabbed as many more and loped howling away across the fens, gloating with corpses, to his dark and watery home.

At dawn his work was known. The cry rose up from

house to house within the walls of the Danish court and a messenger came to the royal bower where Hrothgar, growing old now, rested with his queen. The sun was shot with blood that morning. The air grew heavy with weeping and the hearts of the Danes turned cold. The king hurried to the hall, saw the bloody tracks leading out through the door and across the meadow, walked through the sprung door and across the gore of thirty men that stained the floor and benches. All that morning Hrothgar sat upon his throne and bowed his head beneath a crown of grief.

But there was little time for that, for the next night Grendel murdered again with still worse slaughter—a creature whose mind was driven by harp and song towards one steady, aching desire: to watch the hall by day, to enter and rule it by night. Always he hoped to find at least one man there to ease the infernal hunger that never left him. But the men who had escaped those first attacks found safer beds in bowers away from Heorot, for they had learned that any gathering of good men in the hall at night would be joined by Grendel, bringing his hate as offering to the king and leaving bloody tracks behind as a reminder of his visit.

And so a solitary monster ruled Heorot from dusk to dawn in steady feud, one against them all, until that mightiest of royal seats stood empty at the dying of each day, after the last flare of sun went out beyond the edge of earth. It was a long time; for twelve slow and heavy years the Lord of the Scyldings, King of the Danes, grieved and grieved and bore his endless sorrows. Through somber songs carried out across the mountains and the seas men came to know that in the land of the Danes a creature called Grendel moved nightly with the moon across the darkened moors to visit the king's hall—and lacking the conscience of men, would have no peace with anyone, would never settle his crimes with the payment and repentance that a man of the North would have offered to Hrothgar. He came and slaughtered, a dark shadow of death, hovered and trapped and ambushed old and young alike, and held the misty moors in endless night. He stood in Heorot before the cold hearth and the empty blood-stained benches, and had his way—but he could not approach that throne, kneel and receive gifts from the gracious hands of the king, for the great Measurer of things would not allow it. And so he roamed in endless aching, banished from the light and warmth of mankind.

The king felt that his mind must break with sorrow. Old and wise as he was, he could not find in his thoughts a way to end such terror. Day after day his wise companions sat apart in desperate meditation, searching their minds for help, for just one thing they might do against such swift and heedless murders. At times they knelt and made their vows to idols, prayed to them for help.

"Such was their custom," says the poet, "the hope of heathens. Hell was in their minds then, they did not know about the great Judge of deeds, the Measurer, the Lord of lords, nor knew they how to praise the King of Heaven, Ruler of Glory. Woe to them who shall through wickedness shove their souls into the fire's embrace with no help or consolation forever more; happiness to them who may seek the Lord after death-day and find peace in the Father's embrace."

The great son of Healfdene waited in steady and helpless sorrow, growing older than his years. He could not lift his sword or thrust his spear or swing his broad shield against a creature who would not fight as good men fight, and so there could be no hope. Fate was having its way.

It was then, after those twelve long years, at the moment when my growth was full and my strength complete, when my thoughts turned from the reckless-ness of youth towards the controlled deliberation of a Northern man, that I learned the full story of what was happening in the kingdom of the Danes.

TWO

"HE HEARD at his home about the ravages of Grendel," says the poet, "a good man among the Geats. He was the strongest alive in those days, a noble and powerful man."

I could no longer sit in Hygelac's hall drinking and talking the days away when such a great king had need of my hands. I asked that a good boat be prepared, long but broad in the middle with shallow draft and strong sail, a supple craft of good oak and pine with tall mast and high, coiled prow. I announced that I would sail straight across to the Danish shore as the swan flies.

Though they loved me well, the elders did not discourage me. They studied the signs of sea and weather, nodded, and urged me on. Hygelac was not so eager, for he was friend and uncle as well as king; he asked me not to go, to stay at home where I belonged and let the Danes attend to their own problems. But I reminded him that they had tried their best for twelve years without any luck — then I asked for his blessing and prepared to leave. To sail with me I chose fourteen of the best young men of the nation and ordered tham to sharpen swords and spears and burnish corslets and helmets so that we might step forth into the court of the Danes as clear evidence of the splendor of Hygelac's hall.

I led the way down to the sea where the shore guard waited to see us off. The tide came swirling in as we stowed our weapons and armor by the mast; we shoved out into the sea and stroked away from the cliffs of Götland until the big four-cornered sail was hoisted and the wind snatched at the ship and pulled it away.

We sailed smoothly on in good bright weather, skimming like a huge bird across the top of the water, and the next morning in good time caught sight of the steep shining cliffs of Zealand, center of the Danish kingdom.

The wind drove our ship upon the sand and we lowered sail, leapt into the shallow water and moored our boat to the shore. There we gave thanks to God for our easy voyage and advanced along the beach, corslets clinking as we marched. From the cliffs above, the coast guard had watched us come ashore bearing our bright shields and spears over the gunwale onto the land of the Danes. Now he came galloping down to meet us, drew up and raised his spear above his head, shook it hard and high as a warning signal, and spoke:

"Now who are you in all that war gear, and who has steered such a steep-prowed ship across the waterways? For many years I have kept a close eye on this shore to make sure that no unfriendly visitors come with injurious hearts into the land of the Danes. I have never seen men come bearing shields more openly to this sand; after all, you could not have been sure that we would let you land. And I have never seen a greater man on this earth than that one among you there in his royal corslet. That is no hall-lounger dressed up to look fierce. May the fine look of him never lie!

"And now I will know your tribe before you step any further into the land of the Danes; you may have come as spies for all I know. Hear, then, you possible pirates, my strong opinion: haste will be best in making known where you have come from!"

I stepped forward, raised my shield, and gave him formal answer:

"We are people of the Geats, and Hygelac's hearth-companions. My father, Ecgtheow, was a noble leader well-known among men; he lived many good years, braced the court in his old age, and wise men across the earth remember him well. We have come here with loyal hearts to find your lord, the great son of Healf-dene and protector of his people. Receive us well, and give us good advice!

"We have in fact come here for a special reason,

and there is no need to keep it a secret. If what we have heard is true, and you will know if it is, a certain mysterious and hateful ravager comes bringing terror among the Danes in the dark of night, slaughter and humiliation. I have some generous suggestions for Hrothgar as to how the wise old man might overcome this fiend—if he is ever to get relief from such torment. Otherwise, as long as he lives in that high hall he will suffer a terrible need."

"A sharp watchman has to look out for good or bad intentions in all visitors," he said, "but I can see that this troop comes loyally to the lord of the Danes. Bring your weapons and armor along and I will guide you. Meanwhile, I will order my men to guard your newly tarred ship there at the shore until the time when it will bear you all on its great swan's neck back to the home of the Geats."

We went forward then, leaving our broad ship to ride the anchor ropes. Crouching boar of fire-hardened steel plated with gold rode protectively above our helmets and glittered richly in the morning sun. We mounted the climbing path in single file, our tall spears grazing the limbs of trees, and came out onto the flat meadowland above; from there we could see the gilded gables of the great hall where the king sat waiting for mercy.

The coast guard pointed out the road ahead and turned his horse away: "It is time for me to go; may the Father of us all keep you well in what you are about to do. I will go back to the sea and watch for alien ships."

The street was paved with stones and led us on together. Our corslets, bright with hard hand-locked rings, sang a song of steel as we approached the hall. We set our curved shields against the wall and stood our spears together like an ash-grove tipped with grey; the corslets rang again as the men sat down on the outside.

A proud-looking Dane with gray hair and a rich tunic, his arms circled with twisted gold, appeared at the door. He looked at us and stepped outside to stand facing me.

"Where have you brought all this splendid equipment from?" he asked, "these plated shields and gray-gleaming corslets and good mask helmets? I am Wulfgar, Hrothgar's messenger and aide. I have never seen so many fine-looking strangers, and I think that you have come to see Hrothgar in pride and courage, not as fugitive exiles."

"We are Hygelac's board-companions," I said. "Beowulf is my name. I will explain my coming to your lord, son of Healfdene, if he will grant that we may approach so great a man."

"I will tell my lord that you are here and quickly let you know what the good man says to me."

Wulfgar turned—a man of the Wendels whose courage and wisdom were everywhere known—and went to where Hrothgar sat with his band of earls; he stepped up to face the king, knowing the ways of the court.

"Here have come from far across the sea's expanse a band of Geats. They call their leader 'Beowulf.' They wish to have words with you, my lord, and I would not refuse them. They seem worthy in their splendid armor of the respect of earls; indeed, that king is prosperous and fortunate who could send such warriors to this place."

"I knew him as a boy," said the old king. "His father was called Ecgtheow, a man of the Waegmundings,

and his mother was the only daughter of Hrethel, King
of the Geats and father of Hygelac who now sits on the
Geatish throne. He has come here to see an old friend.
Sailors bringing gifts from the Geats have said that he
has the strength of thirty men in his handgrip. God,
I think, has sent him here in merciful help against
Grendel's terror. I must promise him good treasure
for his boldness. Hurry up, now, tell him to come in
and see us all together, and say that all of these men
are welcome to the land of the Danes."

Wulfgar turned back to the door and beckoned us
in: "My lord asks me to say that all of you are welcome
here. Now you may come inside with your armor and
your shining helmets to greet Hrothgar, but let your
shields and warspears wait here while you talk."

Two men stayed with our weapons and the rest of
us went in beneath the great roof of the hall. We marched
between the long, gilded benches to stand by the great
hearth glowing with warm embers. I stepped forward
to greet the splendid old man who sat upon the throne
of the Danes.

"Good health to you, Hrothgar!" I said. "I am
Hygelac's kin and trusted thane, and I have done many
memorable things in my youth. I heard about Grendel
in my homeland; sailors told me that this best of halls
stands empty and useless when evening light is hidden
away beyond the heavens. And so the best and wisest
of my people urged that I should seek you out, Lord
Hrothgar, because they know of my strength. They
saw for themselves when I came stained with black
blood from crushing and killing five water trolls, when
I slew by night upon the waves as many sprites in revenge for their attacks upon the Geats. And now I shall
settle alone this feud with Grendel.

"I will ask you one favor, King Hrothgar—that you do not refuse me and my men, since we have come so far, the pleasure of purging this mighty hall. I have heard that this monster does not use the weapons of good men in battle. So that my lord Hygelac may be proud of me, I will bear neither sword nor broad yellow shield to that fight, but instead shall meet Grendel with my grip and crush out his life, foe against foe. Death will take the one who must submit to the will of God.

"I am sure that he will eat up the Geats in this hall, if he can, as willingly as he has eaten the men of the Danes. If death takes me, you will not need to hide my head, for Grendel will have me covered with gore, will bear my corpse away to mark the moors with my blood and make a solitary feast of me; in that case, you will not have to worry much about the disposal of my body. Send to Hygelac, if battle takes me, this best of ring-mail that protects my breast; it is the work of Weland and once belonged to Hrethel. Fate will move as it must!"

"You have come to us," said Hrothgar, "in honor of what has passed between our nations. Your father started a strong feud when he slew Heatholaf among the Wylfings, and his people could not afford to keep him for fear of a great war. And so he came across the rolling waves to us. At that time, as a young man, I had just begun to rule the Danes. Heorogar, my older brother, was dead; he was a better man than I! I settled that feud with gifts, sent across the water to the Wylfings old and precious treasures, and your father swore oaths for that.

"It is painful for me to tell anyone what Grendel has done to Heorot with his vicious attacks. Fate has swept away many of my best fighters, diminished the ranks of my dearest men. God could easily put a stop to that! Often have my warriors, after their cups of beer, boasted that they would remain in the hall after nightfall to meet Grendel's terror with the edges of their swords. And then in the morning, in the light of day, this hall would be drenched in blood, all the bench planks covered with gore. And there would be that many less.

"But sit you down to the feast now and think about the victory that will be yours, listen to the tales of great men and whet your mind."

They made room for all of us on the benches. Hrothgar asked me to sit in the place of honor with his sons, Hrethric and Hrothmund. Now Heoroweard, the son of Hrothgar's older brother Heorogar—the dead brother whom Hrothgar so admired—was in the hall and seated with the highest-born young men; but it was another of Hrothgar's nephews—Hrothulf, son of Hrothgar's younger brother Halga, who was also dead—who had the seat of honor beside the king. Thus certain kin are honored above those who would come in strict succession to the throne, as the kings and counselors of Northern tribes think best. Neither Hrothulf nor Heoroweard had much to say but it was clear who had the king's favor. His own sons, of course, were still too young for such a throne.

A servant brought the patterned ale cup and the bright clear liquid. At times Hrothgar's minstrel sang in a clear voice of what he had heard about the old kings and princes of the North who moved in search of conquest to the South, of the strong and handsome deeds of some and the cruelty and treachery of others.

For a little while the Danes and Geats together filled the hall with sounds of happiness.

Then up rose Unferth, bold spokesman of the king who sat at Hrothgar's feet, a place of esteem but also of the jester; in any case, he seemed to hold an honored position among the Danes. He was clearly angry at my presence in Heorot and my speech to the king, and I heard that he did not like to admit that any other man had ever done greater things than he had done. He stood up to face me, drew himself tall, and spoke:

"Are you that Beowulf who had a swimming match with Breca on the open sea, where you risked your lives in the deep water because of a foolish boast? I heard that no one, friend or enemy, could talk you out of such a wretched trick. There you embraced the currents with your arms, measured the sea-road pulling with your hands, sliding over the ocean. The sea was welling with winter waves. You labored for seven nights in the water, and Breca beat you at swimming, had the greater strength. And then at morningtime the sea bore him up in the land of the Heatho-Reams on the west coast of Norway; from there he made it back to his homeland, a beloved man returning to the land of the Brondings where his people lived in strength and wealth. That son of Beanstan carried out his boast against you, and I expect far worse results for you, though you have come through terrible battles, if you dare to wait near at hand through the night for Grendel."

"Well," I said, "you have told a number of things, Unferth my friend, soused with beer, all about Breca and his adventure. But the truth is that I have shown greater strength in the sea and endured heavier punishment among the waves than any other man. We boastfully declared, both of us very young at the time, that we would risk our lives out upon the cold sea, and that is what we did.

"We held naked swords in our hands to defend ourselves against whales as we stroked out from land. He could not swim faster than I could, and I had no wish to leave him behind. And so we were together upon the sea five days and nights until finally the swelling streams drove us apart in that coldest of nights when the north wind hurled against us with terrible waves like battle troops. The creatures of the sea were roused; my strong woven corslet laced with gold and locked hard by skilful hands held me safe against their grappling. Some huge creature snatched me down fast in his grip to the sandy bottom, but it was granted that I might reach him with the point of my sword, and the clash of that fight sent him away through my hand.

"They came at me again and again, loathsome creatures of the deepest sea, but I served them with my precious sword. They had no chance to sit around their banquet at the bottom of the sea, smacking over me. The next morning they lay sleepened by my sword upon the beach, left there by the waves, so that never again would they block the paths of sailors across the broad waters.

"Light broke from the East, God's bright beacon, and the sea grew calm so that I could make out the windy walls of the sea cliffs. Fate often spares the undoomed man when his courage lasts. And so it was granted that I slew nine briny monsters with my sword. I have never heard of another man enduring harder struggles under worse conditions upon the sea streams beneath the vault of Heaven. And yet I survived them all, though weary with battle.

"Then the heaving sea bore me up to shore in the land of the Finns—much further north than the land that Breca found, though you did not mention that. In fact, I cannot remember having heard any similar stories of good swordplay concerning you. Neither you nor Breca has ever performed so courageously with blooded blades—and I will not brag about it much—except that you, of course, killed your own brothers. For that you shall suffer the torment of outlaws in Hell, though your wit may now prevail—at times. Also, Son of Ecglaf, I tell you truly that Grendel would never have worked so many monstrous crimes and humiliations against your people here in Heorot if your magnificence, your grim battle force, were such as you say it is. Instead, he has learned that he need not fear any great swordplay from your people, the 'Victorious Scyldings,' in this one-sided feud. He takes a forced toll, spares no one among the Danes, but rips and slaughters, expecting no fight from the 'Spear-Danes.'

"But I shall soon make clear to him the strength and courage of the Geats through combat. And after that, he who will may go with confidence to drink his mead when the light of morning on the next day, the bright sun from the South, comes shining over the sons of men!"

For the first time in twelve years, Hrothgar allowed himself to be happy. At last, the gray old warrior could believe that help had come to his people. Laughter returned, and the hall rang with hope and harmony in that great company of Danes and Geats.

And then came Wealhtheow down the aisle between the benches, Hrothgar's gracious queen who knew well the ways of the court. In her gold-laced robes she greeted the men in turn, then bore the first cup to the guardian of the Danes, her king of many battles, and urged him to be happy at the feast and generous to his people.

Steep bowls brimming with ale were borne along the benches, and the lovely queen went round the hall to young and old alike, offering cups to her Danes and the visiting Geats, until she came at last to where I sat and offered a cup to me. She was such a queen as queens should be! She thanked God in chosen words that her wish had been granted, that she could now look upon an earl with hope for relief from the crimes against her people. I took the cup from her ringed hands, wondered at the beauty of the great golden collar around her neck, and spoke from my heart to help her courage:

"I decided, when I mounted to the sea in my ship with these Geats at my side, that I alone would work the will of your people, or bow in battle beneath the grip of that murderer. I will earn honor with courage, or find the end of my days in this bright hall!"

She bowed, smiling, and went weighted with gold, queen of her people, to sit by her lord. The feast rang on with hopeful words and the laughter of strong men until at last the son of Healfdene wished to take his evening rest. He knew that from the moment of the rising sun until the darkening shadows of night came looming blackly in beneath the clouds, Grendel had been waiting. The time had come once again, and Hrothgar was weary.

The company rose. Hrothgar gave me a look of

cautious hope; he had suffered too much for too long, and yet he was willing to hope once more.

"Never," he said, "since I first was able to lift shield in hand, have I given the keeping of this hall to any man except now, to you. Take and hold this highest house. If you come through this great battle with your life, you will not lack for good things!"

My wish was honored; all the Danes left the hall. Hrothgar went to take what comfort he could with his gracious queen—too old to fight any longer, he could only walk away from the towering hall he had built and leave its gilded gables in our hands. The King of Glory had set a guard that night against the visitation of Grendel, and I was ready to serve the king of the Danes in my special way, as a champion against monsters.

I took off my good iron corslet, the gilded helmet with the watchful boar heads at the edges of the eyes, and gave them with my patterned sword to one of my thanes, asked him to hold them all for me. I spoke some final words to my men:

"I do not consider myself to be less in combat than Grendel thinks he is, and therefore I will not put him to sleep with my sword, as well I might. Brave as he may be at fighting, he does not know the noble ways of battle, how to cut back against the shield with a sword. We will do without weapons this night, if he dare do battle without them, and God will award the victory as he sees fit."

The Danes had spread the benches with bedclothes and I lay down, put my cheek against the bolster and listened to my men settling down around me. I did not think that they were confident of rising from those beds to go and find their homes again, their people, and the towns where they had been raised. They had heard too much about the slaughter of too many Danes in Heorot where the wine was no more abundant than the blood that had been shed within its walls.

"Yet God would give them luck, help and comfort, that they might through the strength of one man survive," says the poet. "Truly, God ever rules mankind."

THREE

H E CAME in the dark of night, stalking
beneath the shadows. My warriors slept, knowing that
nothing could drag them down to darkness if God did
not wish it to happen. But the thought of all the
killing and heartache that monster had brought to so
fine a hall left no room in my mind for sleep, and
I lay there in a mounting rage waiting for him.

He came from the moors in a towering mist, Grendel gliding, bearing the wrath of God. He yearned to snare another man in that high hall. He moved beneath the dark clouds until he could clearly see that house of wine and gifts, leaved with gold. It was not the first time that he had sought out Hrothgar's home—but never in the days of his life was he to find worse luck waiting there for him.

He came to Heorot, an exile from happiness. The door, strongly bound with fire-hard bands of iron, sprang ajar as he touched it with his hand, and then with a rage for slaughter he swung wide the mouth of the hall. A terrible firelight flared in his eyes as he stepped inside.

He saw there a sizeable band of men sleeping close together, and his heart howled in triumph. His hopes for a good feast jumped high, and he meant to tear the life from the body of each of those men before the break of day. But he was not fated to swallow any more men after that night.

I watched him from pretended sleep to see how he moved. Before I could move he had snatched up one of my men, poor Hondscioh, and began ripping him apart while he was still half asleep. He tore at him with vicious lust, bit into his muscles, drank the streams of blood, and swallowed all the pieces, feet, hands, everything. As he was downing the last of that good man he looked around to find his next meal, and fixed his eyes on me.

So fast he was that he had stepped across to where I was and reached for me before I could rise. I met his hand with mine and returned the grip, then grappled his arm with my other hand. He was a giant of a man-creature with enormous hands that could grab up a warrior by the waist and hoist him high. A great glove, woven of dragon skins and set with curious signs, hung from his hip; I had heard in the old tales that trolls used such gloves to carry away their victims. His eyes, glowing like the smith's fire blown red by bellows, obscured the rest of his face in that dark hall. He seemed deformed, one massive shoulder held high and the other drooping in awful misery.

I could feel the surprise moving into his mind as I tightened my grip. He pulled away towards the door and tried to twist his hand free, and I used that motion to stand up straight and get a good lock around his arm. He gave a great tug then and a deep moan rose in his throat. I tightened my grip. I could feel the fingers cracking under my fist. Grendel jerked frantically towards the door, pulling me along with him. He hissed and tugged, yearning towards the dark fens and meres beyond the world of men, afraid now that he might never return to that region.

He summoned up the last reserves of his strength then and howled to shake the timbers of Heorot. I howled back at him with all the rage in my heart and we rolled and jerked, bounced and careened about the hall breaking the gilded benches and sending them crashing against the walls, ripping the tapestries and scattering the stones of the hearth, setting up such a dense din of awful sound that the Danes huddled together outside the walls in cringing terror at the sound of it. We smashed against the walls until I thought they must surely come down, but the great forged bands of iron held them together. Now Grendel's howling grew higher and more frightened, a horrible sound, and he fought with the added strength of terror, lunging ever towards the doors as I tried to brace my heels to hold him back, knocking pillars from beneath the roof and jerking beams down upon our heads.

All this time my men, very much awake now and ready for battle, kept hacking away when they could get a chance at the lunging fiend—but none of us knew at that time how Grendel had cast a spell upon all battle weapons so that none of them could touch him with harm, no sword could bite that flesh. And so we tumbled and twisted and banged against the walls as swords came ringing down upon the impervious head.

Then something began to give. As Grendel pulled towards the door his arm seemed to grow longer and longer and then I could feel the sinews snapping and the tendons shredding and the ligaments pulling loose as the huge arm bone broke loose from the shoulder, leaving me with the great arm like a log in my embrace as Grendel, a horrible hole where his right shoulder had been, was free at last to lurch bleeding his life out across the moors to find his home again before he died.

I would rather have had Grendel whole in death, but I knew that not even a fiend like that could live for long with such a wound. At least I had done, one way or another, what I had promised to do—if only I could have been quicker, and Hondscioh were still alive. But Fate is Fate, and no man can alter that.

The hall was a wreck; only the hard shell stood fast. First light was lifting in the East as I carried the huge arm out through the sprung door and nailed it high up on the gable beneath the crossed timbers for all to see.

That morning as the sun rode higher and the word spread, men came from all around the country to see the gutted hall and the great bleeding arm and the mortal tracks trailing off across the moors. Horsemen followed the tracks, feeling no sorrow as they read the signs of weakening and pain in the wavering trail of black blood. They followed on across the fens to the mere where Grendel seemed to have gone to earth beneath the water. The mere churned and foamed with the dark blood, they said, hissing with hot gore, and somewhere beneath the surface Grendel lay dying, his cursed soul ready for Hell.

They turned away and then with lighter hearts, young and old, let their nervous horses take the bit and leap away from that dark and misty hole of thrashing water. They spoke well of me, says the poet: "Many a man often said that there was not between the seas over the wide earth to the south or north beneath the sky's expanse a better fighting man more worthy of a kingdom." And still they found praise for their own good king, Hrothgar son of Healfdene, for he was a great man, old and smaller in strength, yet larger in wisdom, a man who had fought in his younger days with the best men of the North.

At times they let their dun mounts leap forth in swift race where they knew the ground to be good, back upon the solid earth away from the moors. At times the king's minstrel, with a head full of songs and a memory for the old tales, found new words and phrases well linked with good sound and sang of my voyage to the land of the Danes, my fight with Grendel, and the cleansing of Heorot. And then he sang of Sigemund, son of Waelsing, and his nephew Fitela who rode with him; together they slew many a monster of the race of giants.

"To Sigemund sprang after his death-day greatest glory," sang the minstrel, "since brave in battle he slaughtered the serpent, guard of the gold hoard."

This was the tale of the dragon slaying, when Sigemund went in alone beneath the grey stone, when Fitela
was not there to help him, and faced the fiery serpent
with his sword, drove the sharp and patterned blade
right through the dragon's underbody with such a
thrust that the point stuck in the stone on the other
side. Thus he earned with his courage the right to the
dragon's treasure: rings and bracelets, swords and
corslets, cups and dishes and banners along the gray
rock walls. He chose what he wanted, that son of Waels,
and loaded his boat with the bright treasure. The dragon died of murder and melted in his own heat.

Then the minstrel brought us back to the Danes in
the skillful circle of his songs: Sigemund, he said, was
the most widely known adventurer among men after the
decline of Heremod. This was the Heremod who died
leaving the Danes lordless for a bitter time until the
arrival of the child Scyld in the boat with the sheaf of
grain.

"Beowulf," said the minstrel, completing the circle,
"is of a different sort, and brings joy and contentment
to men."

Back upon the known paved road the horsemen
again took the measure of their path and let their
mounts leap forth. The morning light had quickly risen
and men came from far around to gaze at Grendel's
colossal arm hanging beneath the gable. Hrothgar came
out from his bower with a troop of men to see for himself, and Wealhtheow followed closely behind him with
a company of maidens.

Unferth was there too—but had nothing to say as
he stood gazing up at the massive arm. The nails, or
hand spurs they might better be called, were more like
steel than anything else, horrible long shafts at the ends

of the cracked fingers. Everyone agreed that not the hardest and keenest of blades, not the oldest and longest tried of heirlooms, could have struck hard and sharply enough to take off that mighty arm. Hrothgar stood before the hall and looked up at Grendel's hand beneath the gilded gable:

"For this sight," he said, "may the Almighty forever receive our thanks. I endured many and many a sorrow because of Grendel; ever may God work wonder after wonder, Heaven's Guardian. It was not very long ago that I expected never to see the end of my grief or receive any help when this best of halls stood stained with the blood of my thanes. The old wise men of the Danes had given up finding a way to fight such a monster. And now one warrior has with the strength of God done what none of us could ever have done. Indeed, if the woman who bore this man were still alive, she could well say that the Old Ruler was kind to her in childbearing.

"And now, Beowulf, best of men, I would have you as a son in my heart. Keep well this new kinship in coming days. Never while I live will you want for the good things of this world, for I have often given lesser men good rewards for gentler battles. May the Almighty reward you for that with his blessing, as he has just now done!"

"We did what we did," I replied, "risked our lives against that unknown force, with willing hearts. I would like to have Grendel himself here for you to see in all his horror. I hoped to bind him in my arms upon a hard deathbed so that he would lie struggling for life beneath my grip, but his body betrayed him; no matter how hard I held to him I could not keep him from getting away. He left his arm and shoulder behind as the price of his escape, but it will do no good and he will get no consolation from it. He will live none the longer, laboring in his sin, for a final sorrow has now wrapped him in baleful death. There he must await, stained with guilt, the great judgment, to see how the bright Measurer will deal with him."

Hrothgar gave orders to repair the hall inside and make it ready for a great banquet. Skillful workers hurried to the court, men and women young and old, and hundreds of hands worked well and quickly against the noonward sun. Soon the shining tapestries, woven with gold, gave bright light to the walls again; hinges were replaced, timbers strengthened, stones reset into the floors and around the hearth; new bench planks brought a forest smell to the great room and soon were leaved with gold and plated with horn for the guests of Heorot. Hrothgar's high-seat was a treasure of gold and walrus ivory and polished oak, and on the beams above dozed falcons and eagle owls.

The fire was lit, the wine was poured, and the meats were turning brown when Hrothgar came to Heorot once again. He sat on his throne and did not watch for the fading light. Beer and ale and mead went round the benches. "I have never," says the poet, "seen a finer band of men carry themselves better in the presence of their king." Hrothgar and Hrothulf sat together and the hall was filled with friends; there was yet no trouble there. Hrothgar's daughter moved along the benches filling the cups; they called her Freawaru, and I heard that she was promised in marriage to Ingeld the Heathobard, son of Froda, as a gesture to strengthen the peace between Heathobards and Danes.

Then Hrothgar raised his hand and called for the treasures to be brought forth. To me he gave a golden banner with finest threads that might have been worked with the hands of elves, so delicate it was; also a helmet, a corslet, and an ancient sword with the hilt wrapped in golden wire and set with garnets on the pommel. Over the crown of the helmet lay a metal tube inlaid with gold and silver wires to dull sharp sword swings in the rush of battle. Next came eight matched gray-brown horses into the hall with plated bridles; on one of them was a gilded and jeweled saddle, the battle seat used by Hrothgar when, young and strong, he had gone forth at the head of his troops against all comers. He gave these treasures into my keeping and bade me use them well.

Finally, to each of the men who had come with me he gave rich gifts, rings and bracelets and knives and cups, old heirlooms from the king's private treasures—and quietly he commanded that Hondscioh's death be met with a heavy payment of wergild in gold coins.

Now the minstrel touched his fingers to the harp and lifted his clear voice in song as the hall grew still. He sang the tale of Finn, king of the tall Frisians, and Hildeburh the Danish queen of Finn, and of her brother Hnaef and her son, of how much sorrow came to this daughter of Hoc in the old days.

Hildeburh sailed south across the sea to be Finn's queen, and to him bore a son. She grew lonely then for the sound of Danes and wished that her brother could see his nephew, for a sister's son is strong in the heart of a Northern man. And so when Finn and his thanes went out for the summer to hold their court in a royal seat called Finnsburh, an invitation was sent to Hnaef to come and spend the summer.

He came with a picked company of sixty Danes, among them Hengest, his finest thane. They were courteously received by the Frisians—a tribe of exceedingly tall and mighty men—and Hildeburh was radiantly happy to see her brother again. There was a fine banquet with excellent wine from the South and the good mead and ale of the North, and precious gifts were presented to the visitors according to the custom of true hospitality. At last Finn stood up to go and Hildeburh, contented with the knowledge that her husband and her brother were friends, followed him. Then all the Frisians left and the hall was given over to the Danes for sleeping.

But there was treachery in the heart of Finn, as it sometimes happens even with the best of men, and he wasted no time in making it known. In the middle of that moonlit night he and his men returned to the hall in full armor with drawn swords.

A Dane was awakened by a gleaming light and ran to tell his lord that the hall was on fire; but Hnaef knew what it was, and jumped up to rouse his men. The minstrel told it well:

Hnaef called to Hengest   hailed his men then:
"No dawning of day this   nor dragon comes here
nor in this high hall   are horn-gables burning—
bright shields are borne here   battle-birds scream
the gray wolf growls   greedy for corpses.
Spears spring at us   space is narrowing
shields take the shafts.   Now shines this moon
heavy with horror;   hate comes forth here
and soon will sorrow   seethe in those hearts.
But wake up, my warriors   wrap on your corselets
let your linden-shields   lean to the fight
stand straight now   and stregthen your hearts!"

They rose up then, the ambushed Danes, and drew their swords. To one door ran Sigeferth and Eaha, and to the other went Oslaf and Guthlaf and Hengest himself. Outside, among the attacking Frisians, old Guthere tried to restrain a young lad named Garulf in this, his first fight, so that he would not be slaughtered before he had a chance to learn the ways of battle—but he was not to be held back. Loudly Garulf called out at the door, asked who was guarding from within.

"Sigeferth is my name," came the quick answer, "of the Secgan tribe. I have come through plenty of bad times and the hardest of battles. What you intend for me is waiting for you here!"

The sound of slaughter ran through the hall, the curved shield boards answered the spear shafts, bodies burst with wounds and the din grew deep. Then young Garulf fell at the hands of Sigeferth, the first man to die, and soon around him many another good warrior lay in death. The raven circled, screaming his hunger. Sword blades flashed a battle light as if all of Finnsburh were on fire.

"Never," said the minstrel, "have I heard that sixty men gave a better fight or better repaid their lord for the clear white mead than the Danes did Hnaef."

They fought for five days, and the Danes held the doors well; not a man of them fell, though at the doors great numbers of Frisians lay in corpse heaps. So the Frisians fell and fell, and Finn could not get into the hall to slaughter the Danes or recover his dead to place them honorably upon the funeral pyre. As the number of Finn's men grew close to the number of Danes, Hnaef was at last caught by a spear and sank to his end. Then Finn called a halt to the terrible slaughter and made a truce with Hengest.

In another situation Hengest would have refused any sort of truce, but he was caught: his men were too weak from thirst and hunger to fight any more, and he needed time. Finn promised that in another hall, back in the central court of his kingdom, equal space would be given to the men of Hengest and Finn. All other things would be equal as well, and each gift from Finn to his Frisians, each ring and sword and bracelet, would be matched with like gifts to the Danes. This he swore in oaths to Hengest, and said that no man of his would ever in any way deny those oaths, nor in any way remind the Danes that they were following the slayers of their lord, since they had no choice; and if any Frisian ever spoke of that matter, then the edge of the sword would settle that man.

The funeral pyre was raised and gold was brought up from the hoard in payment of wergild for Hnaef. Upon the pyre were placed the dead warriors in bloodied corslets, gilded boar glittering above the helmets. Then Hildeburh in double grief ordered the body of her slain son to be placed by the side of her brother Hnaef, nephew at uncle's shoulder. She keened her sorrow as the bodies mounted to the pyre.

The fire swirled up to the heavens and roared above the mound. Heads melted and the wounded bodies burst with springing blood. Then the flames, greediest of spirits, swallowed up those taken away in battle, their glory gone with the smoke.

They went away from Finnsburh, back to Friesland to the central court of Finn and lived together, shared the hall as equals. The Danes would have sailed back to their home, but it was now too late in the year; and so Hengest spent the murder-stained winter against his will among the Frisians. He thought most of the time about his homeland, but could not drive the coiled prow of his ship across the winter sea. The ocean swelled with storm and fought against the wind, and winter locked up the waves with icy chains; the land froze, water stiffened in cold sheets, and ice bridged the bleak sea-road; rime gripped the earth and hail came clattering down in icy grains, snow lashed the air as night shadows deepened.

At last a new year came into the court as it always does, the glorious bright season that ever comes forth at the appointed time, and winter withdrew as the meadows grew fair with flowers. Then Hengest yearned to be away—but he yearned still more for revenge upon the treacherous slayers of his lord. He was ready to remind them with iron of the part they played in his grief, and thought of ways to bring it off. And thus when Guthlaf and Oslaf broke at last beneath their sorrow, and the good warrior Hunlafing solemnly placed a fine old sword in mute suggestion upon his knees, he could hold back no longer.

Spears whined once more above the yellow shields and wolves wailed a terrible song; doomed spirits fled the slain bodies. Shields burst and corslets rang with death. The hall was reddened with the blood of Frisians and Finn himself fell before that vengeance.

The Danes took all they could find from the hall of Finn, treasure and weapons and woven tapestries, good hawks and kegs of wine. They went to their ships taking the daughter of Hoc, Hildeburh of the Danes, bereft of husband and brother and son, with them. Triumph was theirs, but also grief for the loss of their lord.

The song was sung, the minstrel's tale ended. The Danes sat thinking for awhile of that old treachery and wondering about the future years—and then the joy and laughter of the moment came flooding back in and servants poured the bright red wine into the horns and cups as loud applause rose up to the beams.

Then Wealhtheow came up along the benches, her white throat splendid beneath the wide and wonder-worked gold collar, and stood before the high-seat where Hrothgar and Hrothulf, uncle and nephew, sat together: they were yet in peace, each true to the other. Unferth sat at the feet of the king; the Danes honored him and trusted his loyalty and courage, though once he had moved against his kin in the play of swords.

"Take this cup, my lord," she said. "Be happy, and to these Geats speak good words as a man should do. Be generous with them and mindful of rich gifts, of the many fine things you have from near and far. They tell me that you would have their leader for a son. Well, Heorot is cleansed, this bright hall of rings and brace-lets; make good use while you may of your many re-wards, and when you must go forth to meet your destiny, leave to your own kin this kingdom and its people. I know that my good Hrothulf will hold these youngsters in generous honor if you must depart this world before he does. I think that he will reward our sons with all good things, if he remembers all that we did for his well-being and his desires when he was a young lad."

She turned then towards the assembly of noble youth where I sat with her sons, Hrethric and Hroth-mund. To me she offered a cup and two bracelets of twisted gold, a corslet and rings—and then from her neck the great gold collar we had all been admiring. I had never heard of such a treasure, except for the great necklace of tubed and gleaming gold made by dwarfs, it is said, for the goddess Freya, and carried away by Hama as he fled the wrath of Eormanric, King of the Ostrogoths.

I bowed my head to receive the queen's gift. I later gave it to my lord Hygelac's queen, the graceful Hygd, but Hygelac wore it as a sign of his wealth and power when he made that grievous trip to the land of the Franks and Frisians by the river Rhine. Fate took him away then, Swerting's nephew, as his great pride led him among the men of Theodobeorht, son of the great king Theodoric of the Merovingian Franks, where he fell beneath his shield. His armor, his sword, and the great gold collar passed into the hands of the Franks as lesser men robbed his dead body where it lay among the slaughtered Geats.

The hall rang with applause at such magnificent gifts.

"Make good use of this necklace and take luck from it, beloved Beowulf," said the queen, "and this corslet and other treasures from my people. Thrive well, show your strength, and be kind in counsel to these two lads. I will reward you further for that. You have made sure that men from far and near across the wide earth, all that the sea surrounds, the home of the winds and the cliffs, will honor and esteem you forever. Be prosperous while you live, good man. I will wish and grant you many treasures. And be helpful to my happy sons. Here each earl is true to the other, of gentle mind and loyal to the host; these thanes stay well together in ready friendship; these warriors primed with ale do as I ask."

She went then to take her seat. The banquet flourished, warmed with good wine. And then the harp passed to Hrothgar and he showed how a truly accomplished king can handle harp and song as well as sword. He sang a few of the old stories, his favorite tales, and then he touched the strings with a lyric sorrow and spoke of his youth, of many old friends now sleeping in the earth's embrace.

The Danes took fullest pleasure from that banquet, and release from their nightly fear. They did not know what Fate had prepared, what had been arranged long before their time, and so when Hrothgar stood to take his leave, to go with his queen to the royal bower, they wished him good rest and chose to stay the night, as in earlier years, within the walls of Heorot. For me and my men a bower had been prepared so that we might sleep undisturbed.

The benches were bared and spread with bedding and bolsters. One among them lulled with beer bent to his rest, ready and doomed. They set their bright ash-wood shields at their heads, and by them on the benches lay the steep helmets, ringed corslets, and stout spears; swords lay by their sides. It was their custom to be ever ready for war, both at home and abroad, at every moment when their lord might have need of them. They were good men.

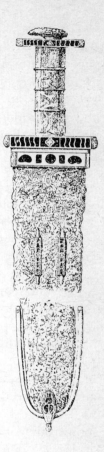

FOUR

"CAIN SLEW his brother," says the poet, "and had to leave the land and the joys of men, marked with murder, to live in the desert country. From his seed sprang whole families of miscreated demons, cursed with the outlawed blood. So Grendel's mother, a wretch of a woman-fiend, was forced to live in terrible waters, joyless cold streams."

Grendel had found at last in Heorot a waking warrior who dared to meet him hand to hand, and that time the Almighty took the battle away from him. Dying he went to find his cold bed, and now his mother, greedy for an answering death, made her miserable way across the fens through the black night towards the great hall where the Danes slept peacefully by the glowing embers. Her strength was less than her son's only so much as the strength of a woman is less than a man's when the gold-hilted sword, hammer-shaped and stained with blood, shears against the boar above the helmet with its sharp edges.

The door flew open and in she burst, in haste to take revenge and be away again. The Danes awoke to see the flaring eyes high above them. Up went the terrible cry and men grabbed for swords and shields—there was no time for helmets or corslets when such terror walked in the hall. But one for one was all she wanted. She snatched up a man—the noble Aeschere, of all good friends between the seas and of all the powerful shield-men, the most beloved to Hrothgar—and was off before any sword could hack uselessly at her head.

A great shout roused the court; they found that the monstrous woman-creature had taken Grendel's mighty arm away with her as she fled; grief and terror filled the hall once more.

"That was not a good exchange," says the poet, "that they should pay on both sides with the life of a loved one."

Hrothgar nearly broke with grief when he discovered that his dearest thane was dead. He called for me at once. I did not know what had happened, but put on my armor and went with my men to his bower, walked inside and stood before the king. The drawn was just before breaking, and I asked if he had spent an agreeable night after so much hardship.

"Do not ask about pleasures!" he cried. "Sorrow has come back to the Danes! Aeschere is dead, Yrmenlaf's older brother, my counselor and companion, shoulder-friend in every battle when we defended our heads together in the clash of troops. So should a man be, as Aeschere was! His slayer here in Heorot was a restless demon, and I do not know where she went from here, gloating over that noble corpse and ready for a feast. She came to avenge the feud you began by killing Grendel yesterday in such violence with your hard grip—and indeed she has carried that feud far, as it may seem to many a thane of Aeschere who aches in his heart for his lord. Now lies dead the good hand that so often did for all of you what you wished.

"I have heard my people say that they have seen two huge monsters roaming the moors beyond the homes of men. One of them, as well as they could make out, had the shape of a woman; the other moved and looked like a misformed man, except that he was much larger than any man. No one knows if they have any parents or if any kin came before them; they are cursed creatures, whatever their origin.

"They live in a secret land, hold to the wolf slopes and windy hills, a perilous fen region where a mountain stream goes down beneath the earth in the dark shadow of a bluff. It is not very far from here to where the mere lies; above the water, clutching tightly to their roots, frosted trees lean over. There every night a wonder can be seen: fire upon water! There lives no son of man wise enough to know the bottom of that mere. Though driven far across the heath in search of thick woods, the strong-horned hart, labored by hounds, will give up his life there on the bank before he will plunge in to hide his head. From it foaming waves lash up darkly to the skies when the angry winds come whirling — the air grows black, and the heavens weep.

"Now it is all up to you again. You do not know that place, that deep den where you might find this creature — seek it if you dare! If you come away from the battle I will pay you well with ancient treasures wound in gold."

"Do not grieve, wise man!" I said. "It is better for every man to avenge his friend than to mourn him too much. We shall all come to the end of this world's life; let him who is able make his glory before death, for that is the best thing for a warrior after his final day. Rise, good King! Let us go quickly to find the trail of Grendel's kin. I promise you this: she will not find a safe hiding place, not under the earth, nor in the mountain forest, nor at the bottom of the sea, go where she will. Have patience this day with your sorrows, as I know you will."

A horse with braided mane was bridled for Hrothgar, and the wise lord rode forth as a king should, in splendid armor. Behind him I marched with the Geats and Danes in a train of shields. The tracks were easy to follow along the wooded path and across the dark moor where the monster had borne the lifeless body of that good man. As we approached the country of steep bluffs I walked ahead along the narrow climbing path past caves where nicors slithered away into places unknown to men. And then I came upon the frosted trees leaning unwillingly out from their clutching roots above the grey stone bluff, the water hurtling down the rock into the angrily seething mere below. The men came up behind me and then we saw together the head of Aeschere lying upon the sloping bank, left there by the monstrous woman-creature as she plunged beneath the surface. The water swirled with gore as we watched, our hearts weeping for Aeschere.

The horn sang a rally song and the men surrounded the mere. As our eyes grew used to the shadows we saw all kinds of squirming sprites and nicors lying upon the banks or sliding out upon the mere, the kind men often see swimming the seas in restless misery. The horn blew again and they plunged in anger beneath the surface. I took a bow from a Dane and placed an arrow in the guts of one; he thrashed in rage against the death that took him as barbed boar spears reached to grapple him and drag him up onto the bank. We had a good look at him then, a great fanged serpent with slimy scales and horns above his eyes; black was his blood, and boiling hot.

This time I put on full armor, for I did not know what I might find at the bottom of that watery prison. Hrethel's corslet, Weland's work, broad and closely locked in rings by those magic hands, would know how to stand strong against the claws that would reach for my life; and the bright plated helmet ribbed with strong iron and wrapped with gilded bands, crowned with the watchful boar who stood against the shearing sword in battle, the work of a wonder-smith, would guard my head.

Then Unferth stepped forward and offered me his sword—a princely gesture from any man. And a fine sword it was. Hrunting, he called it, an ancient weapon tried and proved many times before. The pattern-welded blade with sharp and gleaming edges bore dark serpentine swirls down the center, the mark of suppleness and strength under stress, and it had been hardened many times in the blood of hostile men. It was not the first time that it would be borne in battle, and never, they said, had it failed any man who wielded it well. Unferth spoke no more of the things he had mentioned with his wits warmed by beer. He seemed resigned now to give up to another man the glory he wished to have, for he did not dare to plunge into that troubled water.

I turned to speak to Hrothgar:

"Remember now, great Son of Healfdene, wise King, now that I am ready for this venture, what we talked about earlier—that if I should lose my life in your service, you would ever be as a father to me in memory. Take care of my dear companions if this fight carries me away. And send to Hygelac the treasures you gave me. Hrethel's son will see, when he looks upon those splendid gifts, that I found a good and generous lord to give me rings and bracelets and enjoyed it while I could. Give to Unferth my ancient sword; let that well-known man have its edges. I will make my good name with Hrunting, or death will take me."

I was weary with talking then and eager to find what Fate had arranged for me. I turned and plunged into the thrashing red water and dived for the bottom.

A good part of the morning went past above as I swam straight down. The water was dark and cold and I could barely make out the walls of the deep mere. And then, as I drew near the bottom, a huge black shape came shooting out like a giant crab and I felt the great fingers close around me.

Grendel's mother discovered that a creature from the world of light had come exploring the depths she had so greedily commanded with her son for so many years. She gave a mighty squeeze and the huge nails

jabbed at me like great steel spikes—but Weland knew
how to weave a corslet, and nothing could pierce
through the hard net of locked iron rings.

She was at home, and I in an alien watery place
where I could get no footing, nor could I draw my
sword for the great grip of her hand. She pulled me to
the bottom. Dark shapes darted at me and gnashed
with sharp tusks against the good corslet, but they could
not pierce the mail. And then she tugged me up and out
of the water into a dry cavern.

A pale fire glimmered in the depths of the monster's home and I could make out the roof and the floors
and walls. I got my footing then and jerked my arms
free, drew my sword and swung it with all the strength
I had—it rang a terrible battle song against her head,
but could do no harm. Fine and tested sword that it was,
blade that had never failed at battle, Hrunting failed
this time because the mother, like the son, had cast a
spell over swords.

Anger seized me then and I trusted once again in
my strength. I flung the good sword across the floor and
grabbed at her shoulders, threw her down on her back
—but then she grappled my arms and flipped me over,
pinned me down, snatched a dagger from her waist
and drove it at my heart. Again Weland's wondrous
ring-mail held off the sharp point, but it came again
and again with terrible force and I wondered if my
hour had come.

God had not willed it that way, and with a great
effort I threw her off and leapt to my feet. I saw then
marvelous sword against the wall, a sword for giants
that no other man could have wielded, with broad biting
edges and a great golden hilt. This was a sword that
would heed no charms against it. I heaved it high with

a fury for vengeance and felt the strength of rage in my arms, brought it down in a sweeping crash against the huge neck and felt the blade hack through muscle and bone, straight through the doomed flesh. The head fell to the floor, and the battle was done.

Light filled the cave like the morning sun. I looked around and saw not far away the huge maimed body of Grendel lying in miserable death, and the memory of all that he had done brought a burning anger into my heart. I remembered poor Hondscioh, and the head of Aeschere upon the bank of the mere, and the sight of Grendel lying there with his head still upon his shoulders was too much to bear. I moved to where he lay and heaved the mighty sword a second time, brought it down upon the monster's neck and cut it through.

A wonderful thing happened then. Great and strong as the blade had been, it could not withstand the venomous heat of that horrible blood. It began to bend, and soon was dripping away to nothing like a huge icicle beneath the spring sun when the Father who works the times and seasons loosens the ropes and frosty bonds of winter. And then I stood with the bladeless hilt in my hand, marvelling at the force of that evil blood.

The floor and the walls were heaped with treasures that gleamed and sparkled in the bright light, but I was weary with fighting and took only the great sword hilt and Grendel's colossal head. I longed to see the earth again. I returned Unferth's sword to its sheath and left the cavern, dived straight up through the stained water, moving much faster now, buoyed by victory and light and pulled by the good blue air above. There were no attacks this time; the water was deserted as I soared upward.

Meanwhile, the Danes and Geats above, waiting around the water's edge, had seen the dark blood of Grendel's mother as it flowed from the cavern and rose angrily up to the surface of the mere to boil and swirl there upon the restless water. By then it was midafternoon, and when the wise men of the Danes saw the seething gore they were certain that my blood was mingled with it and that I had given up my life somewhere below in the grip of monsters, never again to stand before the high-seat of Heorot. They convinced Hrothgar that I was dead; the Danes all rose, mounted their horses and rode slowly back toward Heorot, leaving my men alone in their grief.

They sat there with sick hearts, unwilling to believe that I was dead. Then they noticed that the mere had grown brighter, and all the alien creatures had gone into hiding. Soon I came bursting through the surface and swam quickly to the bank where eager hands pulled me from the water and loosened my helmet and corslet. The air was thick with thanksgiving.

Poles were cut and four of my men bore the huge head of Grendel with great labor along the narrow path across the bluffs where the nicors could no longer be seen lying at the edges of their caves. Across the shadowy moors we walked and through the forest of birch and pine, out upon the broad meadows bright with sun and flowers with Heorot shining high and golden bright in the distance. We were proud and happy, though prouder and happier still we would have been to march as fifteen instead of only fourteen.

Again we approached the great door of Heorot, a band of Geats come to visit the king, and this time there were no questions as to who we were or where we had come from, or why. We marched into the hall across the stone floor past the benches and I stepped again before the high seat where Hrothgar sat with his queen beside him.

"We have brought this booty that you look upon here, son of Healfdene," I said, "willingly, as a token of our achievement. That was a terrible fight, a hard and miserable job beneath the water. It would have been short if God had not protected me. I could do nothing with Hrunting, though it is a good weapon— but the Wielder of men granted that I might see upon the wall a marvelous old sword. With a swing of the great blade I slew the guardian of that den, and then the blade burned away beneath the hot blood after I cut off Grendel's head. I have brought the hilt with me as a token of vengeance for the dead Danes. I can assure you now that you may sleep without sorrow with your host of warriors in Heorot, young and old, with no further fear of murder."

Then I gave the hilt to Hrothgar, the work of ancient wondersmiths with scenes in gold relief of the great slaughter flood sent by the King of men to carry away in its terror the race of giants, enemies of God, to a watery end. And below these scenes, in gold runes, was the name of the man or god, a name long forgotten, for whom the huge weapon had been forged and gilded. Hrothgar studied it with care, then nodded and slowly spoke:

"Honest men who remember the past may well say that you were born to be greater than others. Your glory, my friend Beowulf, is now spread far across all lands and raised high above all people. Carry it with forebearance, strength, and wisdom. I will show my love for you, as we spoke of earlier; and you shall ever be a help and comfort to your people.

"Heremod was not so with the sons of Ecgwela, the

honorable Scyldings; he was not a help, but a ravager and murderer of the Danes. He slew in his rage his hearth-companions, shoulder-friends, though mighty God had raised him up above all men in power and wealth and the joys of greatness—and finally he passed alone out of the world of men. Fury and blood-lust grew up in his heart, and he gave no rings to the Danes in reward for their deeds; he lived without joy and suffered for his acts. Take a lesson from that and look to better things; I say this to you as a man old with winters.

"It is a curious thing how mighty God, through His great spirit, hands out wisdom, land and earlship, and control of all things to a certain man. At times He lets the thoughts of the powerful man turn to love, gives him in his home the joys of the earth and a fine court to hold, makes him a ruler of a broad kingdom, so that the man cannot in his earthly thoughts imagine an end of it. He lives in plenty; nothing hurts him, disease or old age, nor does evil care darken his mind, nor sword-hate burn his heart, but the whole world goes his way and he knows no lack—until a great pride begins to grow and flourish within him. Then the soul's guardian sleeps, and the sleep is too fast, the slayer very near at hand who will shoot with evil from the hornbow. Then he is struck beneath his guard with that bitter arrow, an evil command from the alien spirit, and cannot protect himself. What he has held for so long now seems too little, he covets more with a grim heart, no longer gives in splendor the gilded bracelets, and forgets and neglects that world over which God had earlier given him control. In the end the loaned body declines and falls to its doom; another comes to the throne who gives without stint from his old treasures and does not care for terror.

"Guard yourself, beloved Beowulf, best of men,

and choose the better thing: eternal comfort. Let over-
weening pride alone, great warrior! Now your strength
is famous for a time; soon either illness or the sword
will take that strength away, or the embrace of fire, or
the sea's swelling, or the sword's bite, or the spear's
lunge, or terrible old age—until the brightness of the
eye fades and darkens, and death overtakes you.

"I ruled the Danes for fifty years beneath the skies
and protected them against war from many a tribe
throughout the earth, against spears and swords, so that
I did not consider anyone under the expanse of the
heavens as my enemy. And then came the time when
Grendel appeared as my enemy; I took a long and
great sorrow from that visit. Thanks be to God that I
haved lived to see across those years of strife this sword-
bloody head.

"Go now to your seat and enjoy the feast: in the
morning many treasures shall pass between us."

The minstrel touched his harp and sang of strength
and courage, murder and exile, ventures across the
sea in steep ships with coiled prows. The queen and
princess offered cups, and servants kept the horns and
goblets filled with ale and wine and mead. And then it
grew dark again as the night's black cover settled once
more upon the land. The old retainers stood up as
Hrothgar, ready for his rest, arose. And I was ready for
my rest as well. A servant led me to a quiet bower and
saw to all my needs.

That night the great hall towered in peace beneath
a bright moon and men slept quietly within its walls.
After a time the raven cawed at the rising sun and the
morning light came quickly over the earth. I rose and
joined my men, all of us ready and eager to return to
our ship and set sail for home.

We put on our armor and went to take our leave of Hrothgar. I returned Hrunting to Unferth and thanked him for the loan of it, said that it was a fine old sword and would have prevailed against Grendel's mother if any sword made by man could have done so. Then we set our shields once more against the wall outside the door and stacked our spears and went together inside the walls of Heorot.

"Now we must say, we sailors come from afar, that we yearn to return to Hygelac, our lord," I announced to Hrothgar. "We have been well treated and honored here, and you have been a graceful host. If ever I may do more to your will or profit, I will be ready. If I hear across the sea that any of your neighbors come bringing terror to this kingdom, as a certain creature lately has done, then I will bring you thousands of thanes to help. I know that Hygelac, young as he is, will always give me men and support and encouragement that I may bear to your aid a forest of spears if you ever have need of them. And if Hrethric decides to come to the hall of the Geats he will find many friends there; far countries are best sought out by a man who himself thrives well."

"Wise God sent you those words," said Hrothgar. "I have never heard such a young man express himself so well. You are strong in might and wise in mind, clever in words. I think that if spear or illness or sword takes away the son of Hrethel while you are still alive, the Geats will not find a better man to choose for a king and protector of their people. Your mind and heart please me more and more, dear Beowulf. You have made sure that there will ever be peace between Geats and Danes, and have settled whatever disputes there have been between our people, so that as long as I am king there will be gifts between us, many a tribute sent forth across the gannet's bath. The ring-prowed ship shall carry across the sea gifts and tokens of love. I know that our people will be fast united, against our enemies and in favor of our friends, each blameless as in the old days."

And then Healfdene's son gave me twelve more treasures, a hoard of cups and bracelets and jeweled rings, a silver bowl from a far Eastern country, slender tapestries woven with gold and silver and crimson cloth. He bade me seek my lord with this wealth and come back quickly. He seized me by the neck and kissed me, tears streaming from his tired eyes; we both were thinking that we would not see each other again.

We set off along the stone-paved road bearing our rich rewards and soon we could see the ocean from the cliff along which the shore guard came riding to meet us. This time his welcome was quick and warm and we went down to the beach together. We pulled the ship in as far as we could, set a heavy bridge of planks across the gunwale, and loaded the treasures in, horses and all. Then I thanked the guard and gave him a gold-hilted sword so that he would be the worthier the next time he went to the hall to join in the feast. We climbed aboard and shoved off into the swirling tide, hoisted sail and caught the wind for Götland.

FIVE

MY MOTHER was King Hrethel's
daughter. When I was seven years old my father
turned me over to the king to be raised in his court.
He treated me as one of his own sons, gave me
clothing and treasure and saw to my education as
he did for Herebeald and Haethcyn and Hygelac.

Yet I did not show at first any signs of the strength and courage and wisdom for which I later became known, and the Geats did not expect very much from me.

Hrethel was an old man when Haethcyn, trying out a curious horn-bow sent as a gift from the South, let the arrow get away from him; it missed its mark and struck the heart of Herebeald, his older brother. Even unintentional killing draws heavy penalties among Northern people, often death by the slain man's kin; but such things lead on to full war, and usually a payment is made in settlement. Yet in this case, Hrethel could do nothing. His son had been killed by his son— no revenge of any kind was possible, and now he could no longer honestly love Haethcyn. He could only sit and grieve.

It was much like the father of a condemned murderer hanged on the gallows—for executed criminals there is no redress, no payment, no revenge: only grief and shame.

"It is great sorrow for the old man to bear," says the poet, "when his son rides young upon the gallows. Then he sings a mournful song as his son hangs high in comfort to the raven—and he cannot, old and wise as he is, help him. Always he is reminded, morning after morning, of his son's aching absence. He no longer cares to wait for the birth of another son now that this one has been forced away by death. He stands gazing in sorrow upon the hall of the prince, the room where wine had once so richly gleamed now standing empty and wasted, all happiness swept away with the mourning wind. Riders sleep in their graves; no sound of harp or laughter warms the court. The world seems too roomy to the old man, and he lies down upon his couch to sing out his grief and wait for death to come."

So Hrethel with a heavy heart wept for his son, unable to take revenge, unable to punish the son who did the shooting, though he was no longer dear to him. In time his sorrow grew too heavy and he gave up his life to seek the light of God, leaving his kingdom to the son he could not love.

After Hrethel's death the sons of King Ongentheow came down from Sweden, Onela and Ohthere, and near the hill called Hreosnabeorh made a surprise attack upon the Geats; it was a bad day for the sons of Hrethel, but later they had their revenge at a time when I was just too young to take part, and Hygelac was just old enough.

The two brothers, Hygelac and Haethcyn, marched north with a strong army. They took to the waiting boats on the southern shore of the great Lake Vänern and sailed north to gain time and save their strength. Beaching the boats on the northern shore, they gathered forces, scouted the land, and planned their attack. Since they could not know just where the Swedes would be they split their army in two, each brother taking command of half. Then they went their separate ways into the land of the Swedes.

It was Haethcyn who found them near the forest called Hrefnawudu. The Geats attacked at once and drove the Swedes far back; some of them found the queen and captured her. When the old Swedish king heard about that his rage took hold and he led a charge against the invaders. The Swedes swooped in fury down upon the Geats and drove them swiftly back. Ongentheow was shouting for the leader of the Geats; when

Haethcyn stepped forward, the old king closed with him, swung his great sword and cut down Haethcyn with a single, mortal stroke. He rescued his queen and then went after his uninvited quests.

The Geats withdrew into the woods as night came on. Ongentheow settled down nearby and all night long called out to them, telling them how he would handle them when the first light of day came up, how he would cut some of them down with the sword and hang others from the limbs of trees as gifts for the raven and the eagle. The lordless Geats, crouching in the dark woods, gave up to hopeless misery and waited for the sun to bring their death. But then, at first light, Hygelac's horn came sounding through the trees. The battle was terrible, strong on both sides and fatal to many men. At last King Ongentheow, fearful for the safety of his women and children, pulled all his people into an earth-work fortress, taking with him all that he could. But Hygelac's banner rode high across the barrier and the Geats closed in upon the Swedes.

A young son of the warrior Wonred, a Geat named Wulf, found the Swedish king and with a mighty swing of his sword gave the old man a bad wound on his head; but the old man was not called a fierce fighter in idle compliment. He gathered his strength, the blood flowing from the wound at the edge of his hair, and gave back such a blow that Wulf nearly died from it. Then Eofor, Wulf's brother, saw him fall and came to take his place. While others lifted Wulf and bound his head, Eofor swung his blade over the king's shield and sheared down through the helmet; the old king sank then to his death.

Eofor took the corslet, sword, and helmet to Hygelac, who received them well and promised a suitable reward. To both the brothers he later gave large tracts of land and locked gold rings, cattle and horses and swords; and to Eofor he gave his only daughter in marriage.

Soon after that I found my strength and purpose, went off with Breca upon that long swimming match to test them out, slew the sea monsters with my sword, and made a place for myself upon the benches near my king. We became dear friends as well as kin, and then I heard about Grendel.

The sail drew the ropes as tight as harp strings and the sea wind set them humming. The broad ship with its heavy load nosed deep into the white foam sparkling beneath the summer sun and the steep prow rocked up and down against the clear sky. Early on the following day we saw the cliffs of our homeland rising tall and bright from the water.

The guard had been watching for us; we had plenty of help with unloading the treasures and horses across the gangplank. Then we marched up towards the familiar hall towering in the distance. We had been gone for five days.

They were waiting in the hall, Hygelac and his beautiful young queen—young but wise, this daughter of Haereth, generous with gifts from her treasure and her heart to the people of the Geats. "She was not like that other queen, the wife of Offa," says the poet, and indeed she was not. That woman was the terror of her court, so much that no one except her father dared look upon her for fear that he would be caught and bound and put to the sword for his impudence. "That is no queenly way to act," the poet says, "though she be a pretty queen." But then she was sent across the sea to Offa, great king of the Angles who was then still young, and her ways changed. As his wife, said sailors who spread the news, she soon grew calm and became a good and loyal queen, kind to her people and generous. For Offa, son of Garmund of the Hemming kin, was the greatest king between the seas in that country, keen with a spear in battle and quick of hand with gifts to his men. He held his land with wisdom and pushed its boundaries wide. Their son was Eomer, strong in battle.

We crossed the broad meadow glistening beneath the quivering gem of the sun hastening up from the South. Word went ahead and seats were cleared for us. Hygelac gave me the welcome of uncle, king, and dear friend, thankful to see me hale and home again. He seated me by his side, and Hygd poured the bright mead with her white, ringed hands. Hygelac was straining with curiosity.

"How did it go on your trip, dear Beowulf, far across the salt water where you dared to seek such a fight at Heorot? Did you give any help to good Hrothgar in his terrible need? I hated so much to see you go, worried the whole time you were away, for I had no trust in such a venture; I tried many times to talk you out of going to meet that monster, begged you to let the Danes do their own fighting against Grendel. I thank God that I may now see you home and safe again."

"It is well known by now among men, Lord Hygelac," I said, "what a battle we had, Grendel and I, in that place where he had caused such grief among the Danes. I avenged all that, so that none of Grendel's

kin will have any cause anywhere on earth to boast of
that loud dawn, not even the one who will live longest
of that loathsome race.

"I came to the hall and gave greeting to Hrothgar; when he heard what I had come to do, he gave me
a seat with his own sons. There was joy in Heorot; never have I seen a greater elation under the vault of
Heaven. At times the good queen Wealhtheow, who
is ever busy at peace and harmony, moved among the
benches bidding the young men to enjoy the feast,
passing out many a twisted arm ring before going to
take her seat. At times Hrothgar's daughter, Freawaru,
bore cups of ale to the men, jeweled cups from old treasures.

"She is betrothed, I hear, to Ingeld, son of Froda,
as a hopeful gesture for peace between Danes and
Heathobards—but seldom does the battle spear lie still
for very long, though the bride prevail. It will probably
offend the lord of the Heathobards, and each of his
thanes, when a young Danish retainer strides through
the hall in the queen's company, come to be feasted and
enriched by them. On him the fine old sword will
gleam, a treasure sword that belonged to the Heathobards when they were still able to wield weapons, before
they led themselves and their dear companions to
deadly shield play. And then an old warrior warmed
with beer, one who remembers everything, will catch
sight of the fine ringed pommel, the mark of princes,
and his mind will grow grim. He will begin with
mournful tones to try the mood of a young champion
of his people, and say to him these words:

"Can you recognize that good sword now, my
young friend, that dear iron, the one your father bore
to battle beneath his mask-helmet for the last time,

when the Danes slew him and took control of the field after Withergyld lay dead? Now comes some young son of those slayers gloating through the hall and boasting murder, wearing that dear treasure that by rights should be yours.

"He will urge and complain again and again with sorrowful words until the time comes when the young queen's thane will lie sleeping in blood after the sword's bite, forfeit of his life for the deeds of his father. The slayer will easily escape, knowing his native country well. Then the sworn oaths, as in that song of the fight at Finnsburh, will be broken on both sides; lust for blood will well up in Ingeld and love for his wife will cool. Thus I do not think that such a pact of peace or any fast friendship between Dane and Heathobard will be lasting.

"But I will tell more about Grendel so that you may know how our battle of hands came out. When Heaven's gem had glided across the ground Grendel came as an angry guest, evening-grim he came to us where we guarded the hall. All the men had gone to sleep, but I was awake and saw the door fly open as the wretched shape of a huge man came bursting in. So quick was he that he had seized poor Hondscioh, ripped him apart and swallowed him down before I could move. And then he came for me.

"He did not wish to leave the hall empty-handed; he thought to stuff me along with others into the wondrous great glove that hung from his waist. But he found the grip of my hand when he reached for me, and that was the end of his slaughtering. It is too long to tell how I repaid him for all the crimes against the Danes, and the death of Hondscioh. He got away to live for a little while longer, but he left behind his right hand, arm, and shoulder, and dragged himself away to fall to the bottom of the mere. I will tell it all in good time.

"The lord of the Scyldings held a great feast and rewarded me for that battle with many a golden treasure. There were tales and songs. Hrothgar's minstrel touched his harp and sang, and Hrothgar himself sang songs of the mighty men he had known, mourned for the passing of his youth and his strength for battle. And thus we passed the day.

"We slept that night away from the hall, but the Danes slept inside, and grief returned to Heorot with Grendel's mother who came to avenge her son. She made her swift visit, snatched the good Aeschere up from his sleep and carried him away to the mere. Hrothgar's grief was terrible. He could not even lay the body of his great friend upon the funeral pyre, for he had been taken away beneath the mountain stream. Then the king asked again for my help, urged me to show my strength and courage again, and promised me rich rewards.

"I found the bottom of that awful mere, as is now well known. We fought for awhile, and then I carved off her head with a mighty sword, and the water welled with gore. I was not yet doomed. And so the king gave me still more treasures. I will show them to you now, my Lord, for all I have belongs to you. You are my only close kin."

I ordered the treasures to be brought into the hall: the great boar banner of woven gold, the steep helmet, gray corslet, and ancient sword.

"Hrothgar gave me this sword, and asked me to tell you of its origin: he said that his older brother, Heorogar, king of the Danes before him, had held it for long.

He did not give it to Heoroweard, his son, though the lad was loyal to him. Use it well!"

Then the horses were led into the hall: four of them first, apple-dun and swift they were, well-matched. Three others I gave to Hygd, and to her I also gave the magnificent neck ring that Wealhtheow had offered me. Only Hrothgar's horse with his royal saddle I saved for myself.

Then Hygelac commanded that Hrethel's ancient gold-hilted sword be brought forth from his treasure. There was not among the Geats a finer treasure at that time. He laid it across my knees and said I was now the prince of a large domain in that country: seven thousand hides of land, a hall and a high-seat—more than many a king possessed; but Hygelac was still my king, with greater lands and a finer hall, and though I was to rule our people along with him, he was my beloved lord until his death as was his son Heardred after him until his death. I only wish that my lord could have lived longer.

SIX

FIVE WINTERS came and went while the kingdom of the Geats grew richer and stronger. Hygelac had no cause to apologize, for he graced the throne of his kingdom as his brother Haethcyn and his father Hrethel had graced it before him. He was a generous and skillful king—but then, in the spring of that year, he felt the need to sail to the land of the Franks and Frisians to punish them for their hostility. He should have stayed at home to look after his own people, but his heart was high with pride and he ordered the ships made ready, armor tightened, swords sharpened on the stone.

We left the cliffs of Götland in a darkening sea and sailed north around the tip of Jutland and south by the land of the Jutes and the Angles beyond them. Then the sea turned black and mountains of water loomed above our sail. Raven-dark clouds that blocked the heavens came crashing together and the long pale flames cracked the sky around our ships. Thin white spears came hurtling down and clumps of rain punished our faces like hurled sand. The flint-gray waves gathered and mounted into rushing hills and smashed the trembling cliffs with rocks and shells and seaweed, garfish played upon the tall watery ridges and the gray gull circled for signs of slaughter and the stout ropes groaned and stretched and sang in the wind.

My heart was no longer in that trip as we sailed through the storm past the Eider and Ems and into the Zuider Zee. We made our way up the mouth of the Rhine and came to land at a wide flat bend where our boats could be easily beached and as easily shoved out again. There we gathered and marched inland.

The Hetware met us, and then a band of Frisians. We fought a good part of the day. We were strong in that battle and killed many men for every one of ours, so that in the end the few survivors withdrew and left the field to us. In that fight I met the great Daeghrefn, champion of the Franks and Frisians; as it often happened to me, the sword I was using would not stand up under my grip and swing, and the blade snapped. I trusted again in the strength of my hands and gave him a squeeze that reached his heart and stopped it. His sword I bore away, the good Naegling it was called, and it served me well for many years—a famous sword of the Northland.

We raided the halls and carried away all the slaves and women and treasures we could find, took them back to the broad ships and loaded them in. Hygelac stood on the bank and urged each boat to shove into the river and be gone, for he knew that still other Franks lived in that land. He sent me away in a boat with the thirty corslets I had taken in battle, and he was just shoving off when the horn sounded through the woods near the bank.

It was Theodobeorht, the great young prince of the Merovingian Franks with a strong army, sent by his father, Theodoric, son of Clovis, to punish the invaders and recover the spoils. He closed in upon the boats in the shallow water while other boats came down the Rhine and attacked the rest of us. I could see my lord disappear beneath a troop of Franks, swords flailing around him, and there was nothing I could do. They came for my boat and in a few moments had slaughtered all the men with me. In the end there were no boats left except those of the Franks and I found myself alone in their country; all the other Geats were dead. Only the water offered any protection.

As a younger man I would probably have stood there in that final boat, slashing away with Naegling until the fleet of Franks closed in and slaughtered me, thinking that I could never leave a battle in which my lord had been slain. But I thought then mainly of the queen, the new young king who would take the throne now that dear Hygelac lay dead beneath the Frankish swords—and I thought about the wasteful slaughter of all those fine Geats. And so I leapt from the listing boat and reached for the water and stroked strongly away to the north.

I came back alone to the land of the Geats, my heart swelling so with sorrow for my lord and my men that it was hard to draw breath. Hygd listened to me with the courage of her father's blood, and thinking first of the Geats she offered me then and there the throne above her son since she did not believe that such a young lad could defend his kingdom. But I would have none of that. The son of my lord was now King Heardred, and I stood beside him every day to offer my help and my hands when he asked for them.

Then Ohthere was dead, and his brother Onela, king of the Swedes, did not treat his nephews with kindness. These nephews, Eanmund and Eadgils, fled south to our land to ask for help from Heardred, and Heardred took them in. That was the end of him. Onela came and struck so quickly that Eanmund and my young king were both dead before we could rally to fight them. Eanmund was killed by a man of my own people, the Waegmundings—a warrior named Weohstan, serving at that time the king of Sweden. He slew the young prince and took his sword and armor to Onela; Onela said nothing about the fact that the slayer of his nephew stood before him. Instead, he gave the sword and armor back to Weohstan for his own use.

They got away in the dark of night; Hygd begged me not to go after them. There had been much fighting, so many killed—Franks and Frisians, and now the Swedes again. She asked me to take the throne and think about the safety of our people, and I agreed. I, too, had grown weary of slaughter, though I could not refuse to offer men and armor to young Eadgils who would not rest until he had taken revenge upon his uncle and thus revenge for Heardred as well. It seemed a wise arrangement to me, for then all would be satisfied, though bitterly deprived of kin, and there would be peace in our land. And so it was. The Geats and Swedes lived quietly together and gifts sailed often across the lakes from one land to another. King Eadgils of the Swedes and King Beowulf of the Geats sat long and prosperously upon their thrones, and the years turned past.

I ruled the Geats for fifty years, and my thoughts turned inwards.

And then the dragon came. A poor wretch of a slave had fled from his master, an earl of my kingdom, to escape punishment for some offense against a kinsman of the earl. Stumbling in fearful search for shelter below a headland next the sea he blundered through a narrow entrance between rocks and found himself standing in a large room ten feet away from the head of a sleeping dragon. He stood there unable to move, hearing the great heaving winds of breathing and smelling the sulphurous stench, and as his eyes grew accustomed to the dimness he saw the mound of treasure around which the great winged serpentine body lay protectively wrapped.

With the courage of high fear and the desperation of a man who had nothing to lose, he quietly removed a stunningly jeweled cup from the top of the hoard and as quietly backed out again—for with that cup he hoped to buy relief from the heavy punishment awaiting him.

He ran back to his master and laid the cup at his feet, begging for mercy—and the earl, astounded at the richness of the gold and gems and the beauty of the craft, agreed to settle the matter. That is how it began.

"There was many an ancient treasure in that earth-house," as the poet says, "treasure that a thoughtful man of noble blood hid long ago in that place." A man had lived to be the last of his kin and stood alone in the empty hall listening for the sounds that never came. He brought together the treasures of his people and looked at them, knowing that he, too, could use them only for a few brief years before he went to join his kin. He knew of the barrow lying by the headland and carried away the hoard to hide it there. When it had all been laid away, the solitary earl stood by the barrow and spoke his heartwords:

"Hold you now, Earth, now that men cannot, these royal treasures! Good men drew them from you before. Hard battle death has taken away every man of my people—all those men who once sat in the fire-lit hall on winter evenings. I have no one to wear the sword or polish the plated cup—they have all gone away. The good helmet shining with gold shall lose its gilding; polishers sleep, who should burnish it. And so the mail coat that knew the bite of irons over the crashing of shields crumbles like the warrior who wore it; it cannot travel now by the warrior's side. Nor is there joy of the harp, nor the good hawk swings through the hall, nor the swift horse clatters in the courtyard. Baleful death has sent away many a man." Thus the old man mourned, one for all of them, wandered sadly day and night until the welling of death touched at his heart.

The old night-flyer found the hoard—as another poet once said, in counting up the ways of the world,

"The dragon shall be upon the mound, old and wise, and proud in his treasure." He shall seek out hoards in the earth, and there guard the heathen gold, though he will be none the richer for that. And so this dragon stayed for three hundred years with that hoard—until the slave stumbled in.

I was away at that time, an old man scouting the limits of his kingdom. The dragon woke up and discoverd the loss of his cup. Around the barrow he rushed and out through the narrow entrance, circled the mound in furious search for the tracks of the thief who had plundered his hoard. Back into the barrow he slithered and circled the treasures, and back outside around the mound he raced, swelling with fiery rage. He saw no man there but found the footprints and knew that some man had stepped past his head and stolen the cup and run away with it. Thus may an undoomed man escape hard death when he has God's protection.

Again he raced in fury into the mound and searched all around for the missing cup. A cup was missing, one gilded and jeweled cup was gone from the hoard. He could not bear it. He shot outside and circled the mound with snorting fire, then dived back inside and searched for the cup again. Steadily his mind grew hot and heavy with plans for the massive black ruin he would wreak at the end of the day.

He waited in torment for the shadows to grow long, stretched his wings and stoked his flames with the vengeance flaring in his heart. When at last the light of day was dying he waited no longer; he leapt into the air and soared away. Around the sea-wrapped land he flew with great wind-stirring wings, spewing fire across the earth, blasting splendid halls and leaving no living thing in his path. Terror stunned the Geats;

his circling flight over vast stretches of land made plain to the people that nothing would live or stand in that country until his revenge had run its course. And then with a roaring reluctance he shot back to the barrow as light began to show in the sky, leaving the great thrust of land near the sea scorched black with the stench of his hate, halls in black cinders and the bright meadows in smoldering ashes.

Word came to me that the royal hall of the Geats, my throne and treasure, had melted beneath that heat. And no son of Hygelac, nor any son of mine, lived to take the kingdom from my hands. Hygd still lived, but we had made no marriage to produce a son. I wondered if I had in some way failed to live with the right kind of honor, angered the god who ruled over us all. But I could not know that and had but one choice: to step forth once again in defense of my people as I had been taught to do.

I ordered a broad shield of iron to be made, since I knew that no linden-board would be of use against those flames. I would face this monster alone, as I had faced the others. I did not fear the dragon or his flames, nor did I think that he was so great a creature that I could not harm him—but I knew that my life was near its end.

The cup had come to me, sent with the slave who took it so that the poor man could tell me his tale. He was drooping with terror and guilt by this time, but I needed him to show the way. He made the thirteenth man in the small company that set out to find the barrow where the great beast lay hugging his treasure.

We followed the slave across the brittle black meadows to a headland above the sea and he pointed out the barrow below, the hidden narrow entrance of gray rock at the base of the mound. The sea was angry and the day was dim, but there was light, and the dragon slept.

I sat down then upon a rock, gathering strength for the fight. I wished good luck to my men, my heart flooding with strong-sweet memories of my life among the Geats. I could feel Fate coming in across the sea and the air trembled about me with the knowledge that death was standing close.

"I came through many a battle in my youth," I said, as much to the heavens as to the men standing around me. "I remember all of it. I was seven years old when Hrethrel took me from the hands of my father and made another son of me. Haethcyn killed his brother, and Hrethel died of a broken heart. The king of the Swedes slew Haethcyn, and he was cut down by Wulf and Eofor. Ah, Hygelac, my lord and friend! Your bones lay unburned by the waters of the Rhine, and my heart lay with them. But I was ever at your side—you had no need to look for a lesser man among the Gepidae, for I was there, and stronger than them all. I went before you when I could; this sword I bear in battle now, Naegling is its name, I took from the champion of the Franks, the mighty Daeghrefn, in the land of the Hetware nation. I fought each battle well and came away again, and now I will fight for my people if this roaring monster will come from his hoard and meet me.

"I would not bear a sword to this battle if I knew how I might meet him without it, with the grip of my hand as I did with Grendel—but I expect hot flames from this one, scorching breath and venom. I will not budge a footstep from the warden of this mound—Fate will decide what will become of us when we meet. I am strong of heart and will not boast any further."

I sat there for a moment longer, listening to the hiss

and foam of breaking waves and remembering the good green days of my youth while above me long gray clouds slid by like restless thoughts. Then I stood up and said a final word to my men:

"Wait here upon this rise, good friends, to see how the battle goes, and which one of us will better survive with his wounds. This is not your fight, nor is it the measure of any man except myself alone to meet the terrible force of such a monster. I will win this treasure with honor and courage, or this battle will take your lord away."

I raised my shield and approached the entrance to the mound. I stepped just inside the narrow entrance and saw the great stone arches as they faded away into the hot darkness, but a scorching breath of heat came towards me from within and I could not stand there long. It was time for fighting and rage swelled my heart, my arms grew great with courage and I drew a battle breath, sent strong words of challenge singing in among the stones. This the old demon quickly understood, and the time had come.

A blast of withering heat came singeing over me and the barrow rumbled with its force. I swung the heavy iron shield against the blast and drew the good Naegling. Then from the gray stone came the great head striking out with teeth like daggers blinking in the sun and I brought the sword down with a mighty sweep against it. It barely made a dent against those rigid scales.

So the sword, once again, was no good for me. I held the shield before me and waited. There was a great cavernous hiss and a slithering from the mound and then the dragon's head came forth with such a blast of fire that I could not withstand it. I staggered back, the red-hot shield offering little protection and the sword of little use, and turned my thoughts to a summoning of strength to let me stand until the next rush, backing away a little more to let the dragon's neck come further out in the hope that I might have one more swing at it.

The men who had come with me backed steadily away from the first rumble of the dragon. Now they had withdrawn to the edge of a grove of woods nearby, their usual courage overwhelmed by the thunderous monster in the barrow. They could see now that I was losing the fight, but they could not bring themselves to face the fire and the roar. But one of them, a young man named Wiglaf, turned at the edge of the woods and recovered from the shock of the dragon's terror. In his hand he bore the sword that his father, Weohstan, had taken from the dead body of Eanmund, the Swedish prince. For when Eadgils came to the throne of Sweden, Weohstan as slayer of the king's brother felt it wise to move along, and he came then to my kingdom—he was a cousin of mine, a Waegmunding—and joined my court as a valuable and trusted man. There Wiglaf grew up, and stood there now, the last of my kin on earth. He had just come of age, and I had not long before handed over to him the land and hall and armor that his father had held among my people. This was the first time that he had tried himself in battle.

"I remember," he said to the cowering men, "when we sat in the hall of our lord drinking mead, when he gave us rings and armor and places of honor upon the benches, when we boasted that we would quickly and strongly repay him for all of this if ever he had need of us. He chose us especially for this venture because he considered us worthy of the honor, thought us courageous and skillful fighters, valiant men—though our lord thought to do this job alone, since he is the greatest of men and has done the most glorious deeds. Now the day has come when our king has need of the help of good men; let us go and help our battle chief while this terrible flaming terror is such torture to the dear man. God knows that I would far rather have the flames burn my body with my lord's than stand here any longer. I do not think that it would be proper for us to bear our shields back to the court unless we first slay this monster and save the life of our king. I well know that it is not fair payment for his former deeds that he should now suffer this horror alone. We two shall now wield sword and helmet together."

And then he came stepping with full courage through the reeking stench of the dragon's breath until he stood by my side.

"Beloved Beowulf," he said, "remember the boast that you made in your youth, that you would never allow your fame to dimish while you lived. You must now, strong-hearted man, defend your life with all your strength. I will help you!"

After these words the great serpent came lunging out of his den with such a blast of great enveloping heat that he drove us back from the entrance, in one breath burning the shield of Wiglaf right down to the boss. The light lime wood withered and vanished like a dead leaf dropped into the hearth fire. Wiglaf stepped closer then and ducked beneath my broad iron shield, and we waited for a chance to strike.

The head came lunging towards us, the sharp teeth parted, and I swung Naegling above the shield with what strength I had left. The sword broke in two—as good a patterned sword as I had ever seen—but that had happened to me before. The strength in my arms was too much for the blade.

Then came the dragon for the last time and made such an angry rush that the shield was no help. The great beast sank his long teeth into the back of my neck and I could feel the hot poison moving into my body as the blood gushed forth from the wound. But Wiglaf at the same moment leapt in under the dragon's head, burning his hand as he drove his sword deep into the soft underbody. At once the fiery breath diminished and the dragon moved more slowly; then I drew the battle knife at my waist and cut the body in two. Between us, we had killed him.

Then the wound in my neck began to burn and swell; the venom made an aching surge in my chest. I walked over to the entrance of the barrow and sat down against the rock wall. Wiglaf brought water from the stream by the barrow, took off my helmet and bathed my face. I could feel death so near that my thoughts turned now to the Geats who would live after me.

"I would leave this armor to my son if it had been granted to me to have an heir of my own blood. I ruled my people for fifty years. There was no king anywhere near this country who dared seek me in battle. I stayed in my country and took what came, held my kingdom well, and did not go seeking tricks or treacheries, did not swear false oaths. And from all that, sick with deadly poison, I can draw some consolation, for the Wielder of Men will have no need to blame me for murdering my kin when my life leaves this body. Now go quickly, dear Wiglaf, beneath the gray stone to look at the treasure, now that the dragon lies dead, sleeps from his wounds, bereft of his gold. Be quick, so that I may see

the ancient wealth, have a close look at the gold, the
bright gems, and thus give up with greater ease the life
and royal seat which I held for so long."

Wiglaf disappeared inside the barrow and saw then
what the dragon had been so greedily holding for three
hundred years. Everywhere within the mound, on the
floor and hanging from the walls, gold and gems glittered in the dim light. Unpolished cups, their orna-
ments fallen away, sat next to rusted helmets. Twisted
arm rings lay in heaps upon the floor. Then he saw a
golden banner hanging high upon the wall, wondrously
worked with hands, woven with skilful fingers; from it
came the soft light by which he could see the treasures
gleaming. There was no sign of the dragon there; the
sword had taken him away.

Then he quickly scooped up jeweled beakers and
gold dishes and precious swords and hurried back to
tell me of what he had seen, setting his armful of treasures at my feet. I could feel the life in me yearning
away from my aching body and I could no longer clearly see—but he bathed my face again with water and
roused me once more. Then I looked upon the gold and
glittering stones.

"I give thanks to God," I said, "for these treasures
that I look upon, that I was able to win them for my
people before my death. Now that I have paid for this
hoard with my life, dear Wiglaf, look to the needs of
the Geats. I can stay no longer. Tell the Geat warriors
to make a great mound on a high promontory above the
sea, to build it upon the funeral pyre. It will tower
high upon Hronesnaes as a reminder to my people, and
sailors who drive the steep ships far across the mists of
the sea will call it 'Beowulf's Barrow.'"

I took the golden collar from my neck and gave it to Wiglaf along with my gold-plated helmet and Hrethel's corslet, Weland's work.

"You are the last of our kin, the Waegmundings; Fate has swept away all of my family to its will, brave men; I will join them."

SEVEN

Those WERE the last words that I spoke in that life the poet made for me, the last sounds that came from my breast before it lay within the hot welling flames upon the pyre.

Wiglaf sat by my side, weary and scorched by the dragon's flames, trying to wake me up with cold water. He could not accept the death that he saw in my face. And then the ten wretched men who had watched us all this time from the edge of the woods, not daring to join in that terrible battle with Wiglaf—how rich are the rewards of true courage, and how sad the remorse of those who did not have the heart to try—came dragging their shields shamefully towards the barrow, staring at the great smoking beast and wishing too late that they could be kneeling around us with cindered shields and blistered hands and sharing with Wiglaf the quiet fulfillment of promises well kept. He had a fitting name, this good young man: *Wiglaf,* "what survives after battle."

Admitting at last that he could do nothing to change what God had wrought, he turned his sorrow, mounting now to scornful anger, upon the ten wordless men: "He who will speak the truth may well say that the king who gave you the equipment that you stand in there—when he so often among the benches gave to his hall thanes the finest helmets and corslets he could find anywhere, from far and near—that he entirely threw them uselessly away considering their idleness in your hands when battle pressed him down. He had no reason to boast of his troops; but God granted that he might avenge himself alone with a sharp blade when the time came. I could offer him little help in that fight, but I tried to help him anyway beyond my measure; the fire grew ever weaker, came less from the monster's head when I struck him with my sword. Traitors thronged too little about that lord when distress came to him. And now shall the bounty of treasures and the gift of swords, all joy of the native land, all happiness and love, lie dead for all your people. They must wander away deprived of their land and their homes, empty of hand, when noble men get word of your heartless flight. Death is better for any man than a life of misery!"

He soon found a messenger and sent him riding up to the high cliff where the elder Geats had sat all morning with their shields in the seaside fortress by Earnanaes, heavy of heart, waiting for the return of their king or the end of their days. He did not gentle his news, but spoke out clearly for all to hear:

"Now is the generous giver and lord of the Geats on his deathbed, taking a slaughter rest through the dragon's work; beside him lies the old ravager, sick with blade wounds; with his sword the king could not find a way to harm the serpent. Wiglaf sits by Beowulf, earl beside earl, keeping a weary head-guard over loathed and beloved.

"We can expect trouble now when the Franks and Frisians hear of the death of our king. They will remember when Hygelac sailed up the Rhine and raided their lands. Since that time the Merovingians have never felt kindly towards us, nor do I expect peace from the Swedes, since Haethcyn marched into the kingdom of Ongentheow and stole the old king's wife away. Ongentheow killed him for that, but was killed in return, and the end is not in sight: Wiglaf rules the Geats now with Beowulf's armor, but wears his father's sword that slew the brother of Eadgils, the Swedish king. And so I expect no peace or friendship from that land when they hear of Beowulf's death.

"Now it is best that we go quickly to look upon our king, and then bring him who gave us rings to his funeral pyre. Nor shall just one or two of the treasures he gained melt with that good man, but there is a whole hoard of treasure, endless gold so grimly bought, now that he has at last paid for bracelets with his own life. Fire shall cover and consume it—earls shall not wear it in his memory, nor beautiful maidens wrap it about their necks, but all shall walk abroad in alien lands with heavy hearts deprived of gold, now that our leader has laid down his laughter, joy, and song. Reluctant hands shall take up cold spears in the dark mornings. There will be no sound of harp to stir our warriors, but the dark raven will eagerly recite his tales of death above doomed men, will tell the eagle how he had good luck at carrion when he plundered the slaughtered with the gray wolf."

Thus the messenger urgently gave his loathsome news, telling the truth as he saw it. The Geats rose. Sorrowfully they descended from Earnanaes with welling tears to look at wonders. They saw first of all the heap of the dragon lying there by the sea, burned with his own heat; he was fifty feet long. By him stood cups and dishes and precious swords with rusted blades, and lying there on the sand beside them my lifeless body, Wiglaf sitting next to it.

Wiglaf spoke to them: "Often shall many an earl suffer misery through the will of one, as has happened to us. We could not convince our beloved king to avoid the guardian of this gold, to let him lie where he had been for so long and dwell in his lair until the world's end. Our lord held to his high destiny; the hoard is now open, grimly bought; it was too strong a decree that drove him here.

"I was inside there and saw all the treasure in that barrow, a privilege not easily earned. I quickly gathered a load of it and bore it out here to my king. He was still alive then, wise and alert; he spoke of his sorrow and asked that I greet you, bade that you build upon his pyre a high mound, great and prominent, in his memory. Let us now hasten once again to find the heap of marvelous treasures in under those walls; I will guide you so that you may be able to see close at hand the rings and broad gold. Let the pyre be ready when we come out; and then let us carry our lord, that beloved man, to where he long shall take his rest in God's keeping."

Then Wiglaf ordered that many men should bring wood for the funeral pyre: "Now shall the flames grow darkly and consume this lord of men who so often felt the showers of iron when the storms of arrows strongly sent flew over the shield walls, shafts strong in need, swift feather gear following the arrowheads."

And then the son of Weohstan chose seven good men from the troops, went one of eight with them beneath the evil roof; one bore a torchlight in his hand and went in front. They did not have to cast lots to see who would plunder that hoard when they saw unguarded so much treasure; no one was reluctant to bear out of there, and quickly, the precious wealth.

Outside they loaded the treasures upon a wagon, shoved the dragon into the sea and let the waves take the great smoking carcass. Then they bore me to Hronesnaes, and the treasure followed. They built the great pyre and hung it round with helmets and shields and corslets from their own possessions; in the middle of this they laid my body.

They lit the fire; black smoke rose swirling above the circled mound. The wind grew calm and the fire rose higher, melting my body with the gold which lay upon it. The aged Hygd stood with outstretched arms, face to the flames, her hair bound up as her heart was bound in grief, keening my going and weeping her fear for the days to come, slaughter and humiliation and that punishment far worse than death: exile and cold wandering. The flames rose straight up now. Heaven swallowed the smoke.

They built the mound high upon the cliff, tall and broad. First they laid all the treasure I won from the dragon upon the ashes of the pyre, then built a strong timbered roof on columns above it, a large room for my resting place. Around this they worked with earth and rock such a towering mound as was visible far out to sea. They worked for ten days until they were satisfied with it.

Twelve men then mounted their horses and rode around the barrow, sons of kings come to mourn my passing. They gave me praise, as men should give their lord when his life must go from his body. They said, finally, that I was the gentlest and friendliest of worldly kings, the kindest to my people, and the most eager to leave a good name behind him.

II

Translations of Old English Poems

IN THIS part I have given prose translations,
adhering closely to the wording of the texts, of six
Old English poems whose themes and attitudes are
relevant to the themes and attitudes found in
Beowulf. I have made no attempt, as with *Beowulf,*
to bring in additional information, rearrange

sequences, or explain things to the reader. These translations may therefore be taken as fairly literal renditions of the Old English poems.

In preparing these translations I have of course made constant reference to the great collective edition of the entire corpus of Old English poetry, *The Anglo-Saxon Poetic Records,* in six volumes, edited by G. P. Krapp and E. V. K. Dobbie and published by Columbia University Press between 1931 and 1953. Relevant volumes here are the *The Exeter Book* (Krapp and Dobbie, 1936) and *The Anglo-Saxon Minor Poems* (Dobbie, 1942).

THE BATTLE of Maldon was fought in 991
between a Norwegian invasion force and the army
of Byrhtnoth, Earl of Essex (that is, ruler of Essex
and, along with the other English earls of the period,
subordinate only to King Ethelred). The poem,
written in commemoration of the battle, is thus a

very late Old English poem and is technically somewhat looser than earlier poems. But the presentation of the battle is in the best Germanic-heroic tradition established at the beginning of the migration period six hundred years earlier.

Though the names of many Englishmen appear, not a single man of the "Danes" (applied to Norwegians here) is identified. The leader of the Norwegians may or may not have been Olaf Tryggvason, who became king of Norway four years later. In any case, the English lost this battle and Byrhtnoth's thanes, except for a few cowardly deserters, chose to remain beside his lifeless body and fight until they joined him in death.

The Norwegians apparently sailed up the estuary of the Blackwater River in Essex and camped on a triangular island surrounded by marshes and embraced by the northern and southern branches of the river. To get to the East Saxon army on the mainland just below the town of Maldon, the Norwegians had to ford the southern branch, known today as Southey Creek. This could be done at low tide by crossing a narrow causeway which can still be seen today, though it has probably been improved several times. How and why they did cross in this way is explained in the poem. Byrhtnoth's proud invitation is sometimes called "stupid warfare" but the English of the tenth century would not necessarily have thought of it that way.

Something has been lost at the beginning and the end of the manuscript, but probably not much. At the beginning the battle has not yet started, and at the end it is nearly over.

The "he" and "earl" of the first paragraph refer to Byrhtnoth who is ordering "Offa's kinsman," a young warrior, to prepare for battle. The "Pante" is the modern Southey Creek.

The best edition of this poem is that of E. V. Gordon (London, 1937, and New York, 1966).

. . . was broken.

He told every man to give up his horse and drive it far away, to come forth, to think upon hands and good courage. When Offa's kinsman saw that the earl was in no mood for idle sport, he let his beloved hawk leave his hand and fly towards the woods, then stepped to battle. These gestures told that this young man would not cringe in conflict once he had taken up his weapons.

Eadric too wished to serve his lord at battle, and bore his spear to the fight. His thoughts were strong while he was able to lift shield and broad sword in his hands, and he made good the boast that he would fight in front of his lord.

Byrhtnoth rode up and down before his men and toughened their hearts, taught them how to stand and hold, to keep their shields straight and strong in their hands, and never to be afraid. At length he stopped where his most beloved men were standing, his hearth companions loyal as life, and dismounted to be among them.

Then stood on the island's edge a messenger of the Vikings, called sharply across the water to the English earl to make the seamen's message clear: "Sailors have sent me here to tell you that rings and bracelets, quickly offered, might save your lives. It will surely be better for all of you to buy us off than join with us in such a hard rush of spears. We will not have to slaughter each other if you can pay enough; we would make a truce with gold. If you, who are most powerful there, decide to ransom your people, to give to these seamen the payment they judge to be adequate and make peace with us, we will take to our ships with the gold and put out to sea and hold our truce with you."

Byrhtnoth spoke, lifted his shield and shook his supple spear, gave him angry answer: "Do you hear, Sailor, what this army says? We will give you spears as ransom, fatal barbs and honored swords, all kinds of battle gear that will do you no good in this fight. Messenger, take back another message, give your men this unpleasant news, that here stands an unpaying earl with his troops ready to defend the country of Aethelred, my lord, his people and his land. Heathens will fall in this fight. It seems such a shame to me that you should take all that gold and go back to your ships unfought, now that you have come this far into our country. Nor will you get your gold in a gentle way; point and edge shall reconcile us, grim battle play, before we pay you tribute."

The earl ordered his men to bear their shields forth until they all stood on the river bank. Neither army could get to the other across the high water; the tide came flowing in after the ebb, the two streams locked together above the island. It seemed to them too long a time waiting to bring their spears together. They stood along the banks of the Pante stream in proud array, East Saxon warriors facing the ship army. Neither could harm the other except with a lucky arrow now and then.

The tide went out. The sailors stood ready, Vikings straining to battle. Byrhtnoth then ordered a battle-hard warrior to hold the causeway, one called Wulfstan, as strong and brave as the stock he came from; he was Ceola's son, and brought down with his Frankish spear the first man who boldly tried to make the narrow crossing. Beside him stood uncowardly men, Aelfere and Maccus, a strong-hearted pair who had no plans for leaving that ford; they stood as barriers against the enemy as long as they could wield weapons.

When the hateful strangers had seen what bitter bridge guards were there, they began to wheedle, asking for passage across the ford to bring their troops across to the other bank. Then the earl in his great pride allowed them too much land. He called out across the cold water, Byrhthelm's son, as everyone listened: "Now there is room for you; come quickly to us, to battle. God alone knows who will hold this field."

The slaughter-wolves came then, the band of Vikings, not caring about the water; the boatmen bore their linden-shields west over the Pante's gleaming water. There Byrhtnoth stood against them with his men. He ordered a battle-hedge to be made of shields and his army to hold fast against the advance. Battle was nigh then, honor in war. The time had come for doomed men to fall. A cry rose up, the raven and eagle circled, hungry for carrion. A shouting was upon the earth.

Wulfmaer took a wound then, Byrhtnoth's nephew; he was badly hacked with swords and chose a slaughter-rest. But Eadweard evened the score, Byrhtnoth's chamberlain; he swung his sword with full strength so that a doomed Viking fell at his feet, and Byrhtnoth gave him thanks when he had a chance to speak.

The strong-minded men stood tight in that battle, competing to see who would first reach the life of a

seaman with spear point. They stood strong as Byrhtnoth urged those to think about fighting who wished to
earn praise at the Danes' expense.

A battle-hard seaman advanced, drew back his
sword, raised his shield, and stepped before Byrhtnoth.
With the same strong purpose the earl moved to meet
the Viking. Each man had mortal plans for the other.
Then the Viking sent a Southern spear to wound the
lord of warriors. Byrhtnoth shoved with his shield so
that the shaft burst and the spear head sprang away.
He grew angry then and stung the proud Viking with
his spear, guided the point with his hand as it went
through the warrior's throat and reached his life.

Then Byrhtnoth quickly speared another man,
bursting through the mail and straight on to the heart.
The earl was happier then; he laughed, gave thanks
to the Lord for the day's work he had given him.

A Danish warrior let a spear fly from his hand
then; it went right through the great earl's body. By his
side stood a lad not fully grown who boldly pulled the
bloody spear from the earl's breast; this was Wulfstan's
son, Wulfmaer the younger; he gave the weapon back
again and the Danish warrior now lay on the earth
without his life.

Another Dane came up to the earl to take his rings
and bracelets, shield and patterned sword. Byrhtnoth
unsheathed the sword, broad and brown-edged, and
struck against the warrior's mail—but another seaman
reached the earl's arm with his blade and the fallow-
hilted sword fell to the earth; Byrhtnoth could no
longer hold it. Yet he could still speak and hearten his
men to step forth to the fight, though he could no longer stand upon his feet. He looked to Heaven: "I thank
thee, Wielder of people, for all the joys that I have

known in this world. Now I have the greatest need, merciful Lord, that thou grant good to my soul so that it may travel to thee and into thy keeping and peace, Lord of angels. I beg thee to keep it safe from torments of Hell."

Then the heathen warriors hewed him down and both the men who stood beside him, Aelfnoth and Wulf-maer; they gave up their lives beside the body of their lord.

Then some who did not wish to be in that battle turned away from it. First in flight was Odda's son Godric. He forsook his lord, who had given him so many horses, and leaped upon his lord's own horse, upon the royal saddle where he had no right to be. His brothers Godwine and Godwig, with no more taste for battle, fled with him into the protection of the woods to save their lives, and more men than was fitting followed after them, forgetting all the good things their earl had done for them, how he had honored them before the assembled company in the hall, and what they owed him for that. Indeed, Offa had said not long before in a speech before the assembled host that many a man spoke bravely there who later, at the moment of greatest need, would not endure.

And so their leader was felled, Aethelred's earl. His hearth-companions saw that their chief lay dead. The proud thanes stepped forth, uncowardly men, all of them wishing one of two things: to give up life, or to avenge their beloved lord.

Aelfwine, son of Aelfric, a warrior young in winters, encouraged them all with words of honor: "Remember the speeches we made with our mead cups, how we raised up our boasting on the benches together in the hall, spoke strong words about hard fighting?

Now we shall see who is brave. I will make known my noble blood to all men, that I come from a mighty kin among the Mercians; Ealhelm was my grandfather, a wise and prosperous ealdorman. Nor shall the thanes of that people have any cause to condemn me for leaving this army, seeking my homeland now that my lord lies stricken in battle. That is the greatest grief to me; he was my kin and my lord."

He went forward then with feud in his mind and reached a sailor with his spear, sending him forever to the earth. He called to his friends to come forth.

Offa spoke, brandished his spear: "Yes, Aelfwine, you have asked us all to meet this moment of need. Now that our lord and earl lies still upon the ground we must help each other to fight as long as we may have and hold weapons, spear and hard sword. Godric, Odda's cowardly son, has betrayed us all. When he fled to the woods upon that proud horse many a man thought that he was our lord, and so the army on this field was split in two, the shield-wall broken. Cursed be his cowardice, that he put to flight so many men!"

Leofsunu heaved up his shield and spoke in answer to Offa: "I will not flee from here a foot's measure, but will step closer still to avenge my lord. Strong men in Sturmer will have no need to charge me with flight from battle, returning home without my lord; only weapons shall take me away, point and iron." He went forth in anger and gave himself to the fight.

Dunner spoke up then, a simple yeoman, shook his spear and called out to them for revenge: "Now he who thinks to repay his lord may not flinch, nor care for his life."

They all went forth with no thought for their lives. The good retainers, grim spearmen, fought with good

heart and asked God to help them avenge their lord and
fell their enemies. A hostage among them, Aescferth
son of Ecglaf from a great Northumbrian kin, gave
them ready help. He did not flinch at battle play but
urged forth many a spear; at times he shot at shields, at
times he slashed a warrior, and gave hard wounds from
time to time as long as he could wield his weapons.

There in the forefront stood Long Eadweard, ready
and eager. He spoke boastful words, said that he would
not flee a foot's length of land, would not bend from battle now that his better lay dead. He broke the Danish
shield-wall and fought against the men until he had
worthily avenged his treasure-giver upon those seamen
before he lay among the slaughtered.

Aetheric fought as well, Sibyrht's brother, and many
another man; they split the curved shields and fought
for their lives. The shield's edge burst and the corslet
sang a terrible song.

Then Offa, Gadd's famous kinsman, struck a seaman
to the ground; and then he sought the ground himself
beneath the Viking swords. But he had kept his promise
to his lord just as he had sworn to do at the giving of
rings when he said that they both would ride back home
together or fall together with their wounds upon the
battlefield. He lay there now like a true thane beside
his earl.

There was a great clash of shields. The Danes advanced in a battle rage and spears shot through the
breasts of doomed men. Wistan came forth, Thurstan's
son, and slew three men before Offa's life left his body.
The battle grew harder. Warriors stood fast, warriors
fell, weary with wounds. Slaughter lay upon the earth.
Oswold and Eadwold fought on and gave good heart to
their companions.

Byrhtwold spoke, an old man, raised his shield and shook his spear: "Our thoughts shall grow stronger, our hearts keener, out courage greater, as our strength diminishes. Here lies our lord cut down into the dust. Ever may he suffer who thinks to turn away now from this fight. I am old in body; I will not move from here, but will lie down by the side of my lord, by that beloved man."

Then Godric, Aethelgar's son, gave them all courage. He let go many a battle spear to fly against the Vikings, stood foremost among the troops, cutting and striking, until he too fell in battle. This was not that Godric who fled from the fight . . .

"THE WANDERER" and "The Seafarer"
are often and justly included in translations of Old
English poetry. They are much alike in many ways
and draw upon a rich Christian Latin literature for
themes and attitudes, primarily those of the great
patristic writers as re-expressed and modified by

writers in England and Ireland and Spain and Gaul from the fifth century onwards. Yet these poems illustrate two important features of much good Old English poetry: the ability to blend Christian ideas and attitudes with native English traditions in a natural and forceful way, and to turn the borrowed themes into something uniquely Old English.

The structure of "The Wanderer" is a marvel of unfolding from the particular to the universal and back again. I prefer to read the poem as the speech of a single person, with two small interruptions by the poet, and this has been the view of many others before me. Whether or not this is what the poet had in mind, it makes for a clear and effective reading. The rather heavy preaching in the poem's last four lines—which are also, interestingly enough, metrically inferior—may or may not have been tacked on by some copyist, just as the last twenty-two lines of "The Seafarer" may have been.

The final third of *Beowulf* is itself an elegy of great power and beauty and contains two passages strongly reminiscent of "The Wanderer" and "The Seafarer": the sorrowful speech of the "last survivor" as he hides the treasure, and the grief of the old king whose son has been hanged on the gallows.

Two fine recent editions of the poem are available: by R. F. Leslie (Manchester, 1966) and by T. P. Dunning and A. J. Bliss (London, 1969).

"Often the lone one finds God's mercy, though with heavy heart across the seaways he long had to stir with his hands the rime-cold water, travel the tracks of exile. Fate is full determined."

Thus spoke the earth-walker, remembering hardships and terrible slaughter, the fall of friendly kinsmen.

"Often near the break of dawn I had to cry my sorrow alone. There is no one alive to whom I dare describe openly my heart-thoughts. I know for truth that in a noble man is a noble custom, that he bind fast his breast, hold tight his heart-chamber, think what he will. The weary mind cannot withstand Fate, nor the troubled mind give help. And so men yearning for glory will often bind up tight in their breasts all grieving thoughts.

"Thus wretched with care, cut off from my homeland, far from my noble kinsmen, I held back my heart with fetters—that time long ago when I wrapped up my lord in the darkness of the earth and wandered winter-grieving across the icy waves, sought far and near the warmth of a hall and a giver of rings to show me love, comfort my friendless misery, invite me to share his joy.

"He knows who has lived it how cruel a companion sorrow can be for the man who has no beloved friends. The path of exile claims him, not twisted gold, a frozen heart, not earthly splendor. He remembers the hall thanes and gifts of treasure, how his gold-lord taught him to feast in his youth. Happiness fell away.

"He knows, who must live for long without his beloved lord's wise words, when sorrow and sleep together wrap round the lonely wretch, how he dreams that he embraces and kisses his lord, lays his hands and head upon his knee as in earlier days he had often done in happy privilege before the gift-throne. Then the friendless one wakes up again, sees before him the fallow waves, seabirds bathing and preening feathers, frost forming and snow mingled with hail. Then the wounds of the heart are the heavier, grief for his beloved the greater.

"Sorrow comes again when the memory of kinsmen roams through the mind, joyfully hails and eagerly gazes at friends—then the friendly spirits swim away again—they did not bring with them the old familiar tales. Then care is crueller for him who must often send his weary thoughts out across the icy waves.

"And so I cannot think why my mind does not despair when I fully consider the lives of good and brave men, how they stride through the hall and as suddenly leave it for death. Thus the earth, day after day, crumbles and falls. A man cannot be wise until he has known his share of winters in the worldly kingdom.

"The wise man should be patient, not too hot of heart nor hasty of speech, too weak in battle nor too careless, too fearful nor too joyful nor too miserly, nor ever too ready with boasts until he has lived and learned, until he knows well and strongly whither the thoughts of his heart will turn.

"The wise man understands how terrible it will be when all the wealth of this world stands in waste, as now so many walls throughout the earth, by the wind blown, stand covered with frost and snow. Wine-halls moulder, rulers lie stripped of joys. The noble thanes have proudly fallen beside the walls. Battle took some away; the eagle bore one away across the deep sea; the grey wolf got another as his share of the dead; a grieving earl hid one away in the earth. The Shaper of men has thus laid waste this land until, emptied of sounds and citizens, these ancient works of giants stand deserted.

"And so he who deeply considers this dark life and these walls, old and wise of thought, recalls from long ago the slaughter of battle and speaks these words:

"'Where has the good horse gone? Where the young prince? Where the giver of treasures? Where the feast-halls? Where the happiness of gathered men? Alas bright cup! Alas mailed warrior! Alas the splendor of my lord! How time has gone, darkened under night helm as if it had never been.'

"This wall wondrously high now stands where once the beloved host was gathered. Strong spears have taken noble men away, slaughter-greedy weapons, the power of Fate. Storms whip the wall stones, snow storms bind up the earth in winter. Then the dark night shadow comes, grows black, drives from the north a fierce hailstorm for the sorrow of men. All is misery in the kingdom of earth; Fate alters the world beneath the heavens. Here all things are merely loaned: property, friends, family, one's own self. All the framework of this earth grows desolate."

Thus spoke the wise in mind, sat apart in meditation.

"Good is he who keeps his faith, nor shall a man too quickly make known from his heart his misery, unless he first knows how to ease it with his courage. Happy he will be who seeks mercy for himself, comfort from the Father in heaven, where peace awaits us all."

As with "The Wanderer," I prefer to read this poem as the speech of a single person. Some scholars see a three-part division here: first, the words of an old seafarer describing his hardships; second, the words of a young seafarer about to set out; and finally, a heavily Christian epilogue, possibly a later addition. While the "epilogue" may well be a later addition, and is certainly inferior to what comes before both metrically and otherwise, there is no reason not to take what comes before as, like "The Wanderer," a progression from the particular experience of seafaring through the broader implications of such an experience to a general reflection upon the adversity and fragility of earthly life.

The best edition of this poem is that of I. L. Gordon (*The Seafarer,* London, 1960, and New York, 1966).

I can sing a true song of myself, of wandering, how I often bent to bad times in days of sorrowful labor, felt bitter breast-cares, sailed on ship through regions of sorrow across the terrible rolling of waves, where night-watches narrow and grim held me thrall as the ship's dark prow beat the waves past looming cliffs. My feet were gripped with cold, bound up in frost with icy clamps as grief heaved hot about my heart. Hunger gnashed at my sea-weary mind.

The man to whom only fairest things happen on earth cannot know how I followed the tracks of exile in wretched misery, wintered upon the ice-cold sea stripped of dear kinsmen and clamped in a frosty beard. Hail flew in showers. There I heard but the sounding sea, the ice-hard waves clashing.

At times I had the swan's high whoop for music, the gannet's bark and the curlew's trill for the laughter of men, the gull's lament for mead. Storms beat the stone cliffs where the tern shrilled in answer, icy-feathered, and the white-tailed eagle squalled in circles, dewey-feathered. No comforting kinsmen could there console a homeless heart.

He who has known life's joys among his people with splendor and warming wine, who has not felt the pain of such hard wandering, can scarce believe how often I wearily stuck to the sea roads. Night shadows darkened, snow flew from the north, rime bound up the earth, hail fell in coldest grains.

Now thoughts beat like waves against my heart, urge me away to explore the tossing of salt waves upon the deep sea streams. The wishes of the mind urge my heart time and again to set forth, to find a different land far from here. And there is no man upon the earth so proud, nor so generous, nor so keen in youth, nor so brave in deeds, nor so close to his lord, that he is not forever anxious over what the Lord will bring him to in his sea voyage. Nor are his thoughts with the harp, or the gift of rings, or the joys of women, or worldly bliss, or with anything else except the rolling of waves. He is forever longing who explores the sea.

Groves gather blossoms, towns grow fair, meadows brighten, the world quickens. All things then urge the eager heart and mind to ship in one who thinks to venture far away upon the seaways.

The cuckoo urges with his plaintive song; the ward of summer sings, tells of sorrow bitter to the heart. The man blessed with comfort does not know what he who lays the longest paths of exile must then suffer.

And so my thoughts soar out beyond the body's prison over the sea, range far across the whale's home and come back again to me, eager and greedy. The solitary flier calls, compels the heart far out upon the waves' expanse, for the joys of the Lord are warmer to me than this dead loaned life on land.

I do not believe that the riches of earth endure eternally for any man. Always in every case, before his final day, there is doubt as to which one of three will happen: illness or old age or sword-hate will wrench the life away from the doomed departer.

Thus for every man the praise of those who live and speak after him will be the best memorial; this he may earn, before he must go away, through good deeds on earth against the malice of enemies and brave deeds against the devil, so that sons of men will praise him afterwards, and his renown will live afterwards among the angels, forever and forever, in glory of eternal life, bliss among the noblest.

Days are gone, all the splendor of the earthly kingdom. Now there are no kings or caesars or gold-givers as there once were, when such men earned greatest glory and lived in the most lordly renown. All the company has fallen, joys are swept away; lesser men stay behind to hold the world, living in labor. Glory is brought down, earth's splendor ages and withers as now does every man throughout the earth. Age comes upon him, the face pales, the white-haired mourns, knowing that his former lord and all the princes are given up to earth.

The body, when it loses life, cannot swallow sweets or feel sorrow or move its hand or think with its mind. Though the brother will strew the grave with gold for his brother born, bury with the dead rich treasures, they will not go with him; nor may gold give help before God's terror to the sinful soul who hides that gold the while that he lives here upon the earth.

Great is the terror of the Lord, before whom the earth turns aside. He established the firm ground, the corners of the earth and the heavens. Foolish is he who does not dread his Lord; death comes to him before he is ready. Blessed is he who humbly lives; to him comes mercy from Heaven. God will strengthen his mind because he believes in His might.

A man must steer with a strong heart and keep it firm, and be true to his pledges, clean in his ways. Every man should govern with moderation his evil impulses against beloved and hated alike. Though he may not wish the friend he has made to be filled with fire or consumed in the conflagration, Fate is more powerful, God mightier, than any man's conception.

Let us consider where we have a home, and then think how we may go there. And then let us work so that we may go to the eternal bliss where the source of life is in God's love, comfort in Heaven. Thanks be to God that he has exalted us, Lord of glory, eternal Lord, for all time. Amen.

"DEOR" IS a curious little poem composed
primarily of five compact and (to the modern reader)
obscure allusions to famous men and events. *Beowulf*
includes similar allusions in its "digressions" and
they add considerable poignance to the poem; in
"Deor," however, they form the main body of the

poem. I have here translated "Deor" just as it is and have not, as I did with *Beowulf,* included any clarification of the allusions.

Another curious feature of "Deor" is the use of a kind of refrain. In only one other Old English poem — the puzzling but effective poem called "Wulf and Eadwacer" by editors — is such a refrain to be found.

At the end of the poem, after the series of allusions and before the final refrain, are two statements: the first is a general expression of the themes elaborately worked out in "The Wanderer" and "The Seafarer," and the second is a personal statement from Deor the minstrel.

For a detailed explanation of the poem the reader is referred to the edition by Kemp Malone (New York, 1966).

Welund had through serpents a wretched time, a strong-hearted man he suffered hard, had for friends sorrow and longing, winter-cold misery, knew bitter woe when Nithhad laid his need upon him, supple sinew-bonds on the better man.

That has passed, and so may this.

Beadohild was not as sorrowful in her heart over her brothers' death as over her own problem, when she had clearly perceived that she was pregnant; never could she clearly decide what to do.

That has passed, and so may this.

We heard about the moans of Maethhild, the numberless sighings of Geat's wife, that sorrowful love that entirely deprived her of sleep.

That has passed, and so may this.

Theodric ruled the stronghold of the Maerings for thirty years; that was known to many men.

That has passed; and so may this.

We heard about the wolfish thoughts of Eormanric. He ruled widely in the kingdom of the Goths. That was a grim king. Many a man sat bound up in sorrow, waiting for woe, wished often that his reign might be overcome.

That has passed, and so may this.

A man sits sorrowful, cut off from happiness, his mind darkening, and it seems to him that his share of hardships is endless; he may then decide that wise God turns ever through this world, shows mercy to many a man, certain glory, but much woe to others.

I may say this about myself, that I was for a time the minstrel of the Heodenings, dear to my lord; Deor was my name. I had a good place for many years, a loyal lord, until recently Heorrenda, song-crafty man, came into the land rights that the protector of men had earlier given to me.

That has passed and so may this.

IF BEOWULF mentions certain figures
prominent in Germanic lays (Sigemund, Weland,
Finn, and so on) and "Deor" does the same, "Widsith"
probably comes close to being a complete catalogue
of figures known to Anglo-Saxon audiences through
the various kinds of oral poetic tradition. The manner

in which the names are mentioned in "Widsith" certainly implies a general familiarity with them.

The poem tells of a journey taken by Widsith, a professional minstrel, in the company of the lady Ealhild, sister of one Aelfwine, apparently for her marriage to Eormanric. But Eormanric lived in the fourth century, Aelfwine in the sixth. And so the tone and scope of the poem, as it has come down to us, are set: it is an account of the archetypal minstrel, and of all the many rulers of various people, Germanic and otherwise, with whom such a minstrel, given enough centuries of life, would be likely to have had contact.

The first list of kings here is *possibly* the oldest surviving bit of Old English poetry, though the manuscript itself is a part of the *Exeter Book* and thus dates from around one thousand A.D. I have here merely set forth the names of the kings and the tribes as they come in the poem with no attempt at consistency in the modernization of spelling. Many of the names are otherwise unknown, but some are as familiar as our own.

Two fine editions are available: by R. W. Chambers (Cambridge, 1912, reprinted New York, 1965), and by Kemp Malone (Copenhagen, 1962).

Widsith spoke, unlocked his word-hoard, he who of all men had wandered among the most tribes and nations across the earth. Often had he prospered in the hall through gifts of rich treasure. His noble lineage came into him through the Myrgingas. He began with the lady Ealhild, gracious weaver of peace, sought out with her the home of Eormanric, king of the Hreth-Goths and enemy of traitors, from Angeln on the eastern shore. He began then to speak of many things:

"I have heard of many men ruling people. Each man must live according to good customs, lord after lord rule his country thus if his throne is to flourish. Hwala was the best of them for awhile, and Alexander the most powerful of all the race of men: he flourished best of those of whom I have heard tell across the earth.

"Attila ruled the Huns, Eormanric the Goths, Becca the Baningas, Gifica the Burgundians. Caesar ruled the Greeks and Caelic the Finns, Hagena the Sea-Rugians and Henden the Glomman. Witta ruled the Suebi, Wada the Haelsingas, Meaca the Myrgingas, Mearchealf the Hundingas. Theodric ruled the Franks, Thyle the Rondingas, Breca the Brondingas, Billing the Waerne. Oswine ruled the Ilwan and Gefwulf the Jutes, Finn Folcwalding the Frisian kin. Sigehere ruled the Sea-Danes longest, Hnaef the Hocingas, Helm the Wulfingas, Wald the Woingas, Wod the Thuringians, Saeferth the Sycgan, Ongendtheow the Swedes, Sceafthere the Ymbran, Sceafa the Langobards, Hun the Haetwere, and Holen the Wrosnan. Hringweald was the name of the Herefaran's king.

"Offa ruled Angeln, Alewih the Danes. He was the bravest of all those men; but he showed no more the traits of a king than Offa, for Offa carved out the greatest of kingdoms, first among men, while still a youth. No one of his age was more the king. With sword alone he marked a clear boundary against the Myrgingas by the Eider. The Angles and Suebi held the kingdom afterwards as Offa had gained it.

"Hrothulf and Hrothgar held peace together for

very long, uncle and nephew, after they had driven off the Vikings and put down Ingeld's army, cut down at Heorot the host of the Heathobeardan.

"Thus I traveled through many a foreign land over the broad earth; good and evil I knew there, far from my noble kin, followed and served on and on. Therefore I may say and sing a story, make known before the company in the mead hall how high-born men were nobly generous with me.

"I was with the Huns and with the Hreth-Goths, with the Swedes and with the Geats and with the South-Danes. With the Wenlas I was and with the Waerne and with the Vikings. With the Gepidae I was and with the Wends and with the Gefflegan. With the Angles I was and with the Suebi and with the Aenenas. With the Saxons I was and with the Sycgan and with the Sweordwere. With the Hronas I was and with the Dean and with the Heathoreamas. With the Thuringians I was and with the Throwend and with the Burgundians; there I received a bracelet; Gunther gave me there bright treasures as reward for my song; that was no sluggish king! With the Franks I was and with the Frisians and with the Frumtingas. With the Rugians I was and with the Glomman and with the Greeks.

"Also I was in Italy with Aelfwine. He had, as I have heard, the quickest hand of all mankind for doing noble deeds, and the least miserly heart in giving of rings and bright bracelets, that son of Eadwine.

"With the Sercingas I was and with the Seringas. With the Greeks I was and with the Finns and with Caesar, he who ruled over wine cities, riches and all desirable things, and the Roman Empire. With the Scots I was and with the Picts and with the Scride-Finns. With the Lidingas I was and with the Leonas and with

the Langobards, with the Haethnas and with the Haele-
than and with the Hundingas. With the Israelites I was
and with the Assyrians, with the Hebrews and with the
Hindus and with the Egyptians. With the Moide I was
and with the Perse and with the Myrgingas, with the
Ongend-Myrgingas and with the Amothingas. With
the East-Thuringians I was and with the Ofdingas, with
the Ilwan and with the Ostrogoths and with the Idu-
mingas.

"And I was with Eormanric all the time; there the
king of the Goths was generous to me; he gave me a
bracelet, that Lord of men, in which by shilling-count
was reckoned 600 coins of pure gold. That I gave to
Eadgils when I returned home, as a reward to the beloved because he gave me land, my father's estate; he
was lord of the Myrgingas and my protector. And then
Ealhild, queen of the host, Eadwine's daughter, gave
me another one. Praise of her spread through many
a land when I told in song that I knew where the best
gold trimmed queen under the heavens lived and gave
out gold.

"When Scilling and I with clear voice raised up a
song before our victory-lord, loud by the harp the
song sounded; then many a man of proud heart said
in words, they who well understood, that they had
never heard a better song.

"Thence I wandered all through the land of the
Goths; always I sought out the best companions, the
retainers of Eormanric. Hethca I sought and Beadeca
and the Herelingas. Emerca I sought and Fridla and
Ostrogotha, wise and good father of Unwen. Secca I
sought and Becca, Seafola and Theodric, Heathoric
and Sifeca, Hlithe and Ongendtheow. Eadwine I sought
and Elsa, Aegelmund and Hungar, and the proud band

of Withmyrgingas. Wulfhere I sought and Wyrmhere: there was no lack of battle there when the Hreth-Goths near the Vistula woods had to defend with sharp swords the old ancestral seat against the men of Attila. Raedhere I sought and Rondhere, Rumstan and Gislhere, Withergield and Freotheric, Wudga and Hama.

"Those were not the worst of comrades, though I had to name them last. Full oft from the throng flew the whining spear, the yelling spear, into the grim host. Wudga and Hama there ruled the twisted gold, the men and the women.

"So I always found it in my wandering, that he is dearest to his people into whose hands God gives rule over men for life."

And so the singers of men are destined to go wandering through many a land; they speak their need, they say their thanks, and always, south or north, they meet one knowing in song, free in his gifts, he who wishes to raise his reputation before the host of men, to live as a king—until all departs, light and life together. Such a man gains glory, holds beneath the heavens a lasting fame.

THIS BRIEF and fragmentary poem may be
a description of some particular place like Bath in
Somerset, or it may be a kind of composite study of
such places. In any case it is filled with the wonder
of the ruins of Time and is thus a small echo of the
sense of ruin that pervades nearly every line of

Beowulf in the latter part of that poem. Professor Dobbie has called it " . . . the oldest example of formal description in English literature . . . " (*The Exeter Book,* p. lxiv). It is certainly descriptive, and towards the end begins to focus exclusively upon the marvel of the hot baths themselves.

The principal difficulty here of course is what is missing. And yet I have always thought of this little poem as remarkably appropriate in its reflection of the entire corpus of Old English poetry which is in so many ways a huge and impressive ruin in itself.

An excellent edition is available in *Three Old English Elegies,* ed. R. F. Leslie (Manchester, 1961).

Wondrous is this wall stone; things broke it up; city buildings burst apart; the work of giants decays. Roofs are in ruins, towers have crumbled releasing their barred gates; hoarfrost is on the mortar, gables are gaping, rent, collapsed, under-gnawed with age.

The masons lie in the earth's embrace, gone, lost, in earth's tight grip for a hundred generations. This lichen-gray and red-stained wall has known one kingdom after another standing beneath the storms: steep, curved, it fell.

Moulders still the . . . cracked, cloven . . . deeply worn . . . shone, the . . . skill, ancient work . . . crusted with clay.

The mind urged, impelled the swift purpose; determined, in rings, resolute, it bound up the wall roots with wires, wondrously together. Bright were the city buildings, the bath halls, a richness of high gables, great sound of the host, many a mead hall full of man-joys until the mighty Fate changed it all.

The dead fell and fell in days of pestilence; death entirely took away those valiant men; their fortresses have turned to broken pillars. The city crumbled; its rebuilders and defenders fell to earth. And so the buildings grew desolate and the tiles now fall away from the roof's red arch. This ruin fell to the ground in broken heaps where earlier many a man, glad of heart and bright with gold, decked in splendor, proud and wine-gay, shone in his battle dress; he looked upon treasure, upon silver, upon curious gems, upon wealth, upon jewels, upon this bright city of a bright kingdom.

Stone buildings stood; the stream jumped with heat in wide wellings; the wall all enclosed the bright bosom; there were the baths, hot in the heart of it; that was a useful thing.

Then they let flow . . . over grey stone, hot streams . . . to the circular bath. Hot streams . . . where the baths were. Then is . . . that is a kingly thing, how the . . . city. . . .

III

A Note On Editing and Translating Beowulf

IN THIS running account of Old English poetry
I give no credit to the scores of scholars and editors
who have taught me to read and understand it and—
of primary importance—to read the poetry aloud in
a way that must be very close to the way in which
it was read a thousand years ago. References for all

of my debts would take over the pages, and my purpose here is to give an introductory account that will be useful to those who have not studied this poetry before.

In the first place, Old English poetry derives its techniques from a common Germanic oral tradition. The poetry sung by Old English minstrels before the arrival of Augustine in 597 would have been closely similar to the poetry sung by the Goths and Frisians and Burgundians and Swedes: pagan and heroic, strongly stressed, and stored in the minds of minstrels, not in manuscripts. After 597, with the coming of parchment and vellum, ink and quill, and the Roman alphabet, English poetry could be recorded. Eventually much of it was, and much of that has been forever lost; what survives is largely infused in one way or another with Christianity, as would be expected, but the older pagan poetry shows through in several places.

As I have indicated in the introduction to this book, that which may be called specifically English poetry, as opposed to the common Germanic poetry, began at the time of Caedmon, and there is no real reason not to take Bede's story of Caedmon's inspiration, and his merging of the old techniques with the new teaching, as anything but the truth. All of the good Old English poems reflect that merging; some, like *Beowulf*, go far beyond it.

The Germanic poetic technique employs a number of surprisingly rigid rules, but these have been described in so many other places that I will not go into them here. Of more immediate interest here are the problems of editing and translating Old English poetry, and they are many and frustrating. The following passage from F. Klaeber's third edition of *Beowulf*, lines 146b–163, will serve as illustration:

```
                    Waes seo hwil micel;          146
twelf wintra tid    torn getholode
wine Scyldinga,     weana gehwelcne,
sidra sorga;    fortham [secgum] wearth,
ylda bearnum    undyrne cuth                      150
gyddum geomore,    thaette Grendel wan
hwile with Hrothgar,    hetenithas waeg,
fyrene ond faehthe    fela missera,
singale saece;    sibbe ne wolde
with manna hwone    maegenes Deniga,              155
feorhbealo feorran,    fea thingian,
ne thaer naenig witena    wenan thorfte
beorhtre bote    to banan folmum;
(ac se) aeglaeca    ehtende waes,
deorc deathscua,    duguthe ond geogothe,         160
seomade ond syrede;    sinnihte heold
mistige moras;    men ne cunnon,
hwyder helrunan    hwyrftum scrithath.
```

The biggest problem facing modern editors is that
the unique manuscript of *Beowulf* was slightly scorched
along the top and outer edge in a disastrous fire in
Sir Robert Cotton's library in 1731, a hundred years
after Sir Robert's death. For another hundred years
and more the manuscript folios were exposed to crumbling at these edges until finally, about the time of
the American Civil War, the separate folios were
mounted on paper. By this time the crumbling had
obscured all or parts of many words, and the mounting further obscured some readings. It was therefore
most fortunate that, fifty-five years after the fire of
1731, an Icelandic scholar named Thorkelin visited
London and there made a transcript in his handwriting.
He also commissioned a second transcript, imitating
the Old English script, to be made by a professional

copyist. Both of these have thus preserved words and letters which later disappeared through deterioration of the folios.

Thus the modern editor has three manuscripts to consult for difficult readings. How useful the two transcripts have been may be illustrated here. Our passage begins in the middle of the front side of a folio, and down through line 158 there is no real problem in reading it. But as one turns the folio to its back side he finds several words missing at the top and some words only partly legible. Thus the editor, by reading ahead and determining just what verses or parts of verses are missing, by then peeking as well as he can through the semitransparent paper of the mounting, by consulting the two transcripts, and finally by putting all of this together and determining, with his knowledge of Old English poetic technique, what and how much is likely to be missing—after all of this, the editor may reconstruct the fragments and then simply guess at words entirely lost.

Line 159 in this passage was reconstructed in this way so that the last three words—with the help of the two transcripts—became reasonably certain. But this left something metrically to be desired in the first verse, and of the many suggestions offered, the *ac se* ("but the") of Max Rieger in 1871 has generally been accepted.

A different problem is presented by the second verse of line 149, which is missing an important word— in fact, what should be the key word of the line. Many suggestions have been made, but *secgum,* fitting all requirements, is the choice of most modern editors (see discussion below).

It is also the privilege and duty of editors to alter the spelling, and thus the meaning, of certain words if they seem obviously to represent faulty copying. Thus *scyldenda* in line 148, while it makes sense as a word, does not make good sense in this context. What one would expect here would be, in fact, the word *scyldinga,* for the phrase *wine scyldinga* occurs in three other places in *Beowulf,* and closely similar phrases— *helm scyldinga, frean scyldinga, leod scyldinga,* and so on—abound. This alternation points up another helpful feature of Old English poetry and of oral poetic tradition in general: certain stock phrases appear again and again as ready-made "blocks" of words which a poet, improvising and in need of a verse, can bring forth as he recites. As in the above examples, the alliteration of the line the poet is forming in his mind may require an "h" or an "f" or an "l," and he alters the first word accordingly. Considering all this, the editorial change from *scyldenda* to *scyldinga,* capitalized by Klaeber as a proper name, is almost certainly a reconstruction of the original.

The passage is now almost ready for printing. But first the editor must decide which of the Old English characters, if any, he wishes to retain in the printing. And he may decide, as did Professor F. P. Magoun, to "normalize" the text in such a way that a given word will always be spelled the same way and the spelling of the whole will reflect that of a particular period. The passage above retains the spelling of the manuscript as presented in Klaeber's edition but is printed in the modern alphabet.

Finally, then, a translation may be made into Modern English—that is, insofar as such a thing is possible. One may attempt to turn the Old English verses into Modern English verses with the same rhythmical and alliterative pattern, but he will not get far. He may relax somewhat and try for a Modern English alliterative and stressed poetry somewhat reflective of the original, but that too is difficult and only Professor Charles Kennedy, it seems to me, has been generally successful. And then there are all the other approaches: a word-for-word rendering with no attempt at good poetry or prose; a free verse paraphrase; a loose prose translation for both general meaning and easy reading; and many others. Whatever the approach, it is essential that the translator "do his homework" and try to understand as best he can the meaning of each word and phrase in the poem. The passage at hand will serve again, this time to give the reader an idea of the difficulties of translation.

One may begin by copying out the lines and then putting in a close interlinear word-for-word translation which he will then separate from the original and render into readable Modern English. But how does one translate the words?

Most of this passage seems clear enough. The first fifteen lines read smoothly, are made up of familiar words, and contain whole verses which can be found as units again and again in Old English poetry: for example, *ylda bearnum, duguthe ond geogothe,* and one whole line made up of such set verses: *fyrene ond faehthe/fela missera.* One well-read in Old English prose and poetry, and with good editions and dictionaries at hand as well as the new *Beowulf* concordance edited by J. B. Bessinger and P. H. Smith, may feel fairly sure that he *understands,* at least, these fifteen lines. But the first verses in the third-from-last and last lines contain words that give pause to the translator.

Seomade, for instance, is a most interesting word;

and how to translate it? It is a verb in the past tense describing some action of Grendel, that much is clear. One might begin by looking for the same word (ignoring expected variations in spelling) elsewhere in *Beowulf.* In line 302, as Beowulf and his men leave their ship at the beach to march to Hrothgar's hall, the poet says that the ship was *stille* (which in Old English may mean "immobile" or "with little movement") and *seomode* on its rope, fast to its anchor. In line 2767, Wiglaf sees in the dragon's barrow a golden banner *siomian* high above the treasure; from this banner light shone forth so that he could see. Consulting the great *Anglo-Saxon Dictionary* of Joseph Bosworth and T. N. Toller, one finds these references from prose and poetry (I have here merely translated the quotations without giving sources): "Always his [God's] glory stands great and famous and his might *seomath* eternally and forever young over all creation." "It [the light and fire of the descending Holy Ghost] comes through the roof, breaks and burns the hall-timbers, *seomath* steep and curved, climbs on high . . . " "One must ride upon the gallows, *seomian* in death." "The mast shall be fixed in the boat and the yard *seomian.*" "On each side of [the Hebrews] foes *seomedon:* the Egyptians, and the Red Sea." And there are still other references.

Putting all of this together and deriving a composite image from it, we have a rich verb describing Grendel's attitude as he roams the moors, but what one word or phrase will do for the translation? The other word, *syrede,* means variously "lay in wait, ambushed, plotted, trapped," and so on. And so to the translation: "towered and tricked" or "loomed and lurked" or, less ridiculously, "loomed and ambushed"? I finally chose "hovered" for *seomade,* and used two words for *syrede,* thus "hovered and trapped and ambushed." But it was only a desperate attempt to bring the verse alive in modern prose

In the last line is another difficult word, *helrunan.* The trouble here is that the word is not found elsewhere in Old English literature. Cognate Gothic and Old High German forms and Latin glosses all indicate that "witches" or "sorcerers" or simply "hell-fiends" is intended here, and such words will do in translation since these last three verses have the sound of afterthought and are not terribly important to the passage.

It is now time to translate the passage word for word, verse for verse, as literally as possible:

<pre>
                         Was that while great;
     twelve winters' time   grief suffered
     lord of Scyldings   of woes each one
     of vast sorrows;   so that to men became
     of men to the sons   unhiddenly known
     through songs sad   that Grendel fought
     awhile against Hrothgar   hate-crimes carried on
     crime and feud   many of half-years
     continuous strife;   peace not wished
     with of men any one   of host of Danes
     life-bale to remove   with payment to settle
     nor there none of counselors   to expect had occasion
     bright compensation   at slayer's hands;
     but that monster   attacking was
     dark death-shadow   young host and old host
     hovered and snared;   in perpetual night held
     misty moors;   men do not know
     whither hell-fiends   in turnings wander.
</pre>

Old English was an inflected language somewhat similar to Latin or Modern High German, and could often depend upon the endings of words, rather than connective words as in Modern English, for clarification of meaning. Thus *fortham secgum wearth* means "so that to men it became," requiring six words in translation; the *-um* of *secgum* means "to," just as an *-a,* replacing the *-um,* would mean "of (plural)" and would make us translate "of the men." Old English poetry is also repetitious in a certain controlled, stylistic way. Thus *ylda bearnum,* "of men to the sons," is another way of saying *secgum,* using an *-a* and an *-um* to make the relationships between the words clear. And *gyddum geomore* in the next line means "through songs sad" where both the *-um* of the first word and the *-e* of the second indicate that the words are here used in an instrumental sense.

This should be enough to indicate how far removed from the language of the original any translation must necessarily be. The splendid rhythm, natural pauses, and subtle repetition of the verses *fortham sécgum wéarth/ýlda béarnum/úndyrne cúth,* with stresses as indicated, are completely lost. The problem is to render all of this into Modern English, keeping the repetitions, and make it sound palatable to the modern ear.

My translation, as I have already said too many times, is of a particular kind, suited to my particular purpose, and is surrounded and interrupted and interlarded with other material. For a straight translation, one may decide to try for a Modern English poetry somewhat imitative of Old English poetry without too much strain, and come up with something like this:

> It was a long while;
> twelve long winters   he suffered woe,
> king of the Scyldings,   each kind of grief
> and vast sorrows . . . .

The translator may alternately turn this passage into prose, something like this:

"It was a long time. For the length of twelve years the lord of the Scyldings endured his grief, every kind of woe, vast sorrows."

Beyond this there are endless possibilities. As of this writing there are at least ten translations in print — some prose, some poetry, some both. But all of them are based upon the labors of generations of scholars and editors, and are themselves, if they are honest translations, the products of considerable labor. Choosing between them is therefore largely a matter of personal taste. They are all trying to do the same thing: to make available to the modern reader, who cannot read the language of his earliest literature, its greatest product.

Rinehart Editions